Tales Told in Holland

Edited by
Olive Beaupré Miller

Illustrated by
Maud & Miska Petersham

Publishers
The Book House for Children
Chicago

THE STORIES in this book are chiefly Dutch legends and folk tales which I gathered from Dutch books bought in different parts of the Netherlands and translated with the help of a Dutch-speaking secretary. It is called "Tales Told in Holland" because in the United States the child most frequently hears the Netherlands referred to as Holland. Nevertheless, this book includes at least one tale from each of the eleven provinces which form the kingdom of the Netherlands—Groningen, Drente, Overyssel, Gelderland, Friesland, Utrecht, North Holland, South Holland, Zeeland, North Brabant and Limburg.

Fanciful folk tales come from the little known heath and fen country of Groningen, Drente, Overyssel and Gelderland where the folk must make up for the barrenness of their land by the fruitfulness of their fancy. Realistic tales are from the green and fertile provinces of Friesland, Utrecht, North Holland, South Holland and Zeeland, with their typical Dutch scenery—flat green fields, windmills, little red-roofed houses, dykes, and black and white cows—a country so satisfying that the good folk accept the world as their two eyes behold it and do not fly away on the wings of fancy but are quite as matter-of-fact as their excellent Edam cheese. And so the stories go on through the province of North Brabant to Limburg, the land of ancient sagas of Charlemagne, bordering his capital of Aix-la-Chapelle, and full of the atmosphere of romantic legend which arose when the Netherlands formed a part of the Empire of Charlemagne.

Expressing the Dutch sense of humor we have tales of the wise men of Kampen, who do all the foolish things done in the Netherlands, and that Dutchest of Dutch puppets, Jan Klaasen with Katryn, his wife. We have also Tyl Ulenspiegel, the beloved Dutch clown, and those ridiculous German simpletons, the Hannekemaiers, who come every year to help with the harvest in Holland and furnish the Dutchman a butt for the merriest of his jokes.

In addition to these folk tales, all the high spots in Dutch history are touched upon by means of stories. For example, tales of Tyl Ulenspiegel, the clown, whom nearly all Dutch children know, took on, through much telling and retelling over many generations, incidents from the period of William the Silent and the dramatic struggle of the Netherlands for independence from Spain. Thus the stories concerning Tyl have a setting of that most important period. Telling briefly the story of "The Black Tulip" by Alexander Dumas permits me to deal with the tulip craze in Haarlem and the fate of the brothers De Witt. Another story brings in the young Countess Jacqueline and Philip the Good of Burgundy, who stole the Netherlands from Jacqueline and won the title of "Good" by being surpassingly bad. Thus the greatest characters in Dutch history, as well as its most interesting periods, become alive to the child.

One cannot deal with Holland at all without speaking of its art, for even Italy itself has scarcely contributed more to the art of painting than Holland. Holland's artists are her most outstanding feature—so in our work we have tales of Rembrandt, Van Dyck, Franz Hals, with a word about Jan Steen, Gerard Dou, Vermeer, and others of the lesser artists.

The illustrations for this book, like those in "Nursery Friends from France," were done by Maud and Miska Petersham who made a separate journey to the Netherlands, traveling through the eleven Dutch provinces, as I myself had done before them. Thus we made sure that all details of architecture and customs should be authentic. And we were especially careful about the details of peasant costumes which vary in different districts and are all too often garbled up in picture books about the Dutch. Too many artists have seized a cap or bonnet from one district and mixed it up to suit their own artistic fancies with an apron, kerchief or other detail of dress from an utterly different district, presenting a hodgepodge which gives no true idea of the costumes which have made Dutch peasants so picturesque. In "Tales Told in Holland," each story or poem from a different district is illustrated with the actual costume which characterized that district.

Thus this book was designed to reveal in a way most interesting to the child, as much as possible of all sides of Dutch life—Dutch history, Dutch art, Dutch literature, Dutch geography, Dutch customs, and, withal, the Dutchman's sense of humor, his love of cleanliness and thrift, his sturdy independence and the character of his fancies.

Altchen and Berend-John

A Tale from the Province of Overyssel

THERE lived once in a poor little house on the edge of a lonely heath in Overyssel, a pretty lassie named Altchen and her father, Bartes Aarnink. Now Altchen had a sweetheart, a poor young farm-hand called Berend-John. He was not much blessed with money, young Berend-John, and that's a fact. He knew more of cows and butter and pigs than of golden florins, but, for all that, he was a Sunday child with a sunny temper, and he knew the lilt of a merry song, and the joy of a strong right arm, better than the next fellow, so that none could help but love him. That is to say, none could help but love him, who loved sunshine and life and joy better than golden florins, and Altchen loved him with all her heart. As to old Bartes, her father, however, well! that was a different matter,—quite a different matter.

Bartes Aarnink was a poor peasant. A cow and a pig or two were all his worldly possessions. To him it seemed the most wonderful thing in

The costumes used in this story are those of the town of Staphorst in Overyssel.

the world to be the master of florins, and he hadn't even a few extra coppers to jingle in his pocket.

Now it chanced at just this time that there lived near by a certain rich old farmer, named Scholte, and Scholte, like Berend-John, came a-courting the pretty Altchen.

"Ah, there's a husband for my daughter!" said old Bartes to himself, "rich as a nobleman,—aye, even richer. There's the man to put florins and ducats into my empty pocket!"

And he would have nothing but that Altchen should make ready at once to marry old Scholte.

Well, of course, it was true that Scholte was richer than a nobleman, but it was also true that he was uglier than a screech-owl! He had long, thin legs like a stork's, a short puffed-up body, monstrously fat, and tiny pig-eyes, deep sunken in rolls of flabby pink flesh. He looked like a huge sack of meal, going about on two slender twigs!

And if he had been ugly in appearance only . . . . .

But no, he was as stingy as a mole, and as covetous as a kite. He loved nothing but money. All his life long he had thought only of getting, getting, getting. What did he know of giving! He had snatched, and grabbed, and clutched, he had heaped up, and counted and hoarded, till the chink of florins was the only music in life that could give him any pleasure. Never in all his days had he sung a merry song. When he walked on a road full of sunlight with birds above, and the heath a sea of purple bloom about him, he thought only of his florins. When a veil of floating mist hung over the fields and all was still and lonely with the wonder of a mystery, he continued to think of nothing but his florins, florins, florins!

It was not until he grew old that Scholte began to think he would like to buy something with his money. Then he looked about and made up his mind to buy himself a wife. He would take to be Vrouw Scholte none but the prettiest girl in the neighborhood. That was how he had chosen Altchen.

After that it was "Give your daughter to a rich man, friend Bartes," and "Sons-in-law with treasures like mine are none too easy to find!" and other such arguments all sounding more of clinking florins than of the simple music of love.

Well, Bartes didn't need many arguments to make him say yes to old Scholte's wooing. No, not he! The florins did all the courting necessary. Before Altchen even knew what was going forward, she found herself shut up tight in the house, kept fast under lock and key.

"You shall never see that lout of a Berend-John again," cried her father. "But you shall spin and sew and make ready for marriage with a man of means, a man as rich as a nobleman!"

Little did Bartes care that Altchen wept and begged and said she would rather have the fattest of their grunting pigs for a bridegroom. He was her father; he could command! He would give her away to whomsoever he chose.

Thereafter, no man was permitted in the house but that meal sack on twigs, old Scholte. And old Scholte grimaced and screwed up his face with his button nose and his pig-like eyes, as he tried to smile on the lovely Altchen.

O me and O my! . . . . .

Often in those days there were tears in Altchen's pretty blue eyes,— often and often, tears. And as to poor Berend-John, why, what was he to do? He roamed sadly about Altchen's home, trying to catch even a glimpse of her. If he could but have seen her little finger, or the tiniest wisp of her hair! If he could have heard her voice for a single moment, it would have been enough. So foolish was his heart, so tender, so innocent his love. Look! What did he care that village folk who passed, made fun of him as he lingered by the house? He thought only of Altchen. Didn't he know that she was young like himself and her love for him was as sweet, as foolish as the love that he showered upon her?

Now one night Berend-John, lost deep in thought of his trouble, was wandering along by a little creek that watered the last fertile land on the edge of the heath. Suddenly an idea struck him. Out there in the dark somewhere stood a willow tree. Day in and day out, that willow tree looked just like any other willow tree that grew along the roadside, gracefully nodding its head and rustling its silver leaves in the breeze. Only if a man in passing said something mean or false, would the willow tree grow in a twinkling till it became as big and overpowering as a mighty oak. Then would issue from it a breath swifter and stronger than the stormwind, and a voice like thunder. And if he who passed had said something too wicked, indeed if he had but thought something wicked, there would come rocks from the tree pelting through the air, till the wicked one ran for his life. Now the reason for all this was, that there dwelt in the willow tree, the Willow-Man. This Willow-Man disliked what was ugly and mean, and he loved what was good and beautiful. The real business of his life was to help Sunday children.

As Berend-John walked along by the creek on this particular night, he remembered all this. He remembered that he was a Sunday child and he said to himself in a twinkling: "I shall ask the Willow-Man to help me."

No sooner had he said this quite distinctly, than he heard a soft rustle in the air, like a ripple over the water,—still, still as the far-away lap of the sea at night, and yet it was very near.

At that sound, Berend-John scarcely knew whether to be glad or to run away. In a moment, perhaps, he would see the great Willow-Giant towering above him. But just then a voice as kind as a mother's said:—

"Don't be afraid, Berend-John. I am the Willow-Man and you are a Sunday child. I shall help you. There are alack! all too few Sunday children on earth. Most men toil and strive and labor to find happiness, and in so doing they never find it at all. But the Sunday children are always happy, though they take no trouble about it whatever. Most of them, I'm sorry to say, don't know what to do with their happiness. They play with it, and fritter it away, and make nothing of it. You, Berend-John, I believe, will enjoy it seriously and to some good purpose. For that reason I shall help you."

At these words, Berend-John fell on his knees for gratitude, but the kind voice went on:—

"You need not kneel. Look! I shall make a light so we can see each other better."

And the Willow-Man turned around seven times and stamped three times with his foot on the earth. Then there sprang up suddenly out of the ground, a clear, white flame. It did not spread, but kept on burning brightly just where they were.

Berend-John saw the Willow-Man very plainly. Was this the Willow-Giant, the huge, towering Willow-Giant? An ordinary, good-natured little fellow he seemed, just like a farmer from over Windesheim way. He might have come from any one of the villages near the Yssel

River. Could such an everyday little man be more powerful than Bartes Aarnink and Farmer Scholte together? Berend-John looked very doubtful. But the Willow-Man asked simply:

"Can Bartes Aarnink and Farmer Scholte make fire?"

It was true,—they could not.

"You are right," said Berend-John. "If anyone can help me, you can."

"Trust me," said the Willow-Man, and he put his hand on Berend-John's blond hair to bless him. "Trust me! I shall help you!"

Even as he spoke, the fire went out as suddenly as it had sprung up and all became dark. The Willow-Man had vanished. Berend-John held his breath, listening. No leaf rustled, no ripple moved. The dark was like a deserted hall,—not the trembling of a breath of air, not the swaying of a branch. No more did the voice of the Willow-Man fall on Berend-John's ear, but within his soul and spirit it kept on ringing with joyous promise, sweet and clear like a little bell.

Through the days that followed, Berend-John felt safe and secure. Though no reason for his faith could be outwardly seen as yet, he knew

11

that the Willow-Man would help him; he had but to wait in patience to find out how this would come about.

Now the third evening after Berend-John had met the Willow-Man, Bartes Aarnink was home alone with his daughter. Dusk had fallen in the little room, and Bartes sat bent over his spinning wheel, that he might be able to use all the last faint gleams of light. That was poor land of Bartes Aarnink's on the edge of the heath. There is rich land in Overyssel, but there is poor land, too, and many a peasant like Bartes, whose farm yielded little return, made both ends meet by spinning. When it was altogether dark, Bartes rose.

"It is time for bed," said he. "Well-to-rest, my child!"

Ah, little did the stubborn old peasant know that he would not rest much that night! Just as he was pulling back the curtains of his bed, which was built like a cubby-hole into the wall, he heard outside, quite near the house, the anxious lowing of a cow.

"The cow's broken loose! The cow's broken loose! She's out of the barn!" he cried, and off he hurried in great excitement, calling as he went, "Here, boss! Here, boss! Here, boss!"

No sooner had he crossed the threshold of the door than he saw the form of the cow looming up just ahead in the dark.

"Here, bossy!" he cried with a coaxing, wheedling quaver.

But his cow did not heed his voice. With a little kick and plunge, she made off suddenly across the road and out on the heath,—out, out and away into the blackness of the night. As she went, she bellowed softly, as though she were afraid.

Now that was bad, very bad! There might be wolves on the heath. Quickly the farmer followed the cow. The faster he went, however, the faster went old bossy, as fast and as fast as though she had been bewitched. Moreover, as she ran, all of a sudden, like magic, a light appeared on the tip of her tail and went switching back and forth like a will-o'-the-wisp in the darkness. At sight of that weird little light, Bartes stopped short in his tracks.

"What is the world coming to?" he thought.

Stranger still, when Bartes stopped, the cow stopped and bellowed mournfully as if waiting. But the very moment he set out again, thinking he was almost upon her, off she ran as before, swinging her luminous tail behind her. Farther and farther from home she led him, over lonely plains of peat and heather, of sand and pine trees, for it is no pretty cozy country that, no land of green grass and canals and wind-mills and cattle at the brink of reedy pools, soft and gracious like the rich and placid fields of North Holland. It is lonely there on the heath of the Overyssel—a barren, desolate land to go racing through in the dark, with a swaying light like magic, leading one on and on and on.

Now at almost the very same time of night when Bartes set out on his strange adventure, a queer thing happened to Farmer Scholte. He had gone about spying at every door and locking the house up carefully, and was about to lie down on his miserly bed of dry leaves. At this moment he heard a sound which he could distinguish from every other sound in the world. Chink, chink, chink—gold coins knocking against each other!

Farmer Scholte jumped up and unbolted the door. Less than twenty feet away from him on the ground lay a gray bag, which was wriggling all over as though it had been filled with scores of little mice. From inside came the sound of gold coins, chinking and jingling and tinkling, dashing and clashing and pushing against each other, and singing in hard, shrill little voices:—

> "Wolly-wee-wee-wee,
> Wolly-wee-wee-wee,
> We'd like to go walking
>   Far and afar,
> To find out where
> The gray wolves are!"

Farmer Scholte stooped over and snatched at the bag, his eyes glistening. He almost had it—his hand was just on it, when suddenly it jerked away, as though a string had been fastened to it, and some mischievous urchin had been playing a trick on old Scholte. There it went leaping like mad, pell-mell, hop, skip and jump. A full twenty feet it bounced like that, and then of a sudden it tumbled down again, plump! on the ground, while the ducats inside giggled and laughed and sang their everlasting:—

> "Wolly-wee-wee-wee,
> Wolly-wee-wee-wee,
> We'd like to go walking
>   Far and afar,
> To find out where
> The gray wolves are!"

Now you may well believe that Farmer Scholte was both astonished and confused, but one thing he knew for certain,—catch that bag of ducats he must! Never would he let such a fortune as this run away from him and escape. As he saw it, lying there flat on the ground, he thought to get it by stealth. With sly and silent feet, he crept up to it, noiseless as any sneaking cat. When he came near, he crouched in the dark and pounced. But, again, just as he had the treasure almost in his grasp, it bounced out of his hand, and hopped off for another twenty feet, the ducats giggling and laughing more mockingly than before.

In this remarkable manner, Farmer Scholte, too, was led on and on and on over the heath through the dark, he following the impish bag, while Bartes Aarnink followed the cow. The only one of the three, so deeply concerned with Altchen, who was not out chasing wildly after some will-o'-the-wisp of his own selfish desires on that eventful night, was Berend-John.

Berend-John laid himself quietly down on the cool grass near Altchen's house and thought to go to sleep. It was good to be able to dream near Altchen since he could not reach her. Slowly all the world faded out of his thought and there remained to him only the warm and fragrant sense of his love. But just at that very moment when he would have fallen sound asleep, someone touched his shoulder. He sprang to his feet, startled, then he smiled, for it was the Willow-Man who had wakened him.

"Go straight to Altchen," said the Willow-Man. "The door is not bolted. She is home alone."

Berend-John was so mightily astonished that he could only stutter and stammer. He wished to say, "Thank you," but he could not. Head

over heels he ran! Off to the homestead he ran, like a rabbit to his hole. When Altchen saw him coming, she called out in dismay that he must not come in—her father and Farmer Scholte might appear at any moment with stout clubs to drive him away. But before two words of all this could pass the young lassie's lips, Berend-John had her fast in his arms.

And now, pray tell, what need was there to fear that Bartes and Farmer Scholte would return before the Willow-Man wished it? Bartes was still running after the cow and Farmer Scholte was pursuing the hopping purse with a rink-kink-kink and a kink!

They ran through the woods and the trackless heath, they plunged through brooks and water-ways like madmen without aim. In the cloudless, dark blue sky the moon shook with laughter, the stars danced. It was a sight to make a donkey laugh, a sight to make a scarecrow dance. The Willow-Man followed the two. He played the lute, he cut crazy capers for pure fun and merriment, the serious Willow-Giant! with a hippety hop and a skip!

But suddenly all grew quiet, the moon held his breath, to see what would come next. Then the Willow-Man swayed his magic wand through the air. At that, the cow stopped short, the money bag fell plump on the ground. Not a single ducat so much as jingled.

"Ha!" thought Bartes, "now I have her," and he plunged madly toward the cow.

"Ha!" thought Farmer Scholte, "now I have it," and he plunged madly toward the bag.

But at that very moment the cow and the bag suddenly flew up high in the air and vanished. The two men ran straight into each other's arms.

"Hokus-pokus-pilate-stop!" shouted the Willow-Man. Then everything began to shine and laugh again, especially the moon.

Bartes and Farmer Scholte looked at each other in blank amazement, but magic had changed them entirely. The Willow-Man had made each one look to the other just like Berend-John. Each was sure, indeed, that it was Berend-John who had plunged into his arms, and then they let out all the hatred for Berend-John that each had been storing up in his heart. They took their big clubs and began to strike at each other, beating like blacksmiths on iron, and each one thought he was beating Berend-John.

There! There! They clubbed each other black and blue until they both fell to the ground and lay as still as fallen logs. Whack and crack and batter out there on the heath, but all this while, back in the room where Altchen and Berend-John sat happily together, were only peace and quiet and tenderest affection.

Now in the morning, Bartes and Farmer Scholte came to themselves at the very same moment. At the very same moment they sat up and looked into each other's eyes. Each had his own appearance again and neither looked to the other in the least like Berend-John.

Said Bartes Aarnink to himself, "It was that black-hearted old rascal, Scholte, who beat me black and blue last night."

Said Scholte to himself, "It was that black-hearted old rascal, Bartes Aarnink, who beat me black and blue last night."

With that, each one would have sprung up and been at it again with his cudgel, but alas, they both found themselves too battered up to begin their fighting anew. With angry looks they parted.

"It will be a cold day before I give Altchen to that hot-headed old fire-eater," said Bartes to himself.

"It will be a cold day before I make myself son-in-law to that hot-headed old fire-eater," said Farmer Scholte to himself. So each went his separate way, and neither so much as looked back for a single glimpse over his shoulder.

And that's the end of that!

With a fiddle-dee-dee and fiddle-dee-don,
There's a wedding of Altchen and good Berend-John!

Their descendants live on the homesteads in Terwolde and Nybroek to this very day. They know the merriest tunes and dance the jolliest dances. They like witty stories and they love love.

16

The Mermaid of Edam

A Tale from the Province of North Holland

T happened once that a mighty storm broke the great dykes, those giant walls which hold back the Zuyder Zee. Plunging and rolling, the angry waters rushed in over the flat green meadows of North Holland that lie lower than the sea. The tall windmills waved their arms in vain,— they stood knee-deep in water. The little toy villages poked up their red roofs in huge astonishment above the flood, and the cowbells on the scattered cattle rang out a wild tonka-tonka, discordant in alarm.

When the waves began to recede somewhat, and the green meadows showed themselves again, smiling in the sunlight, certain young lassies from the city of Edam set out to carry fresh water to the cows in the distant pastures, for the poor things had had nothing to drink for hours, with only salt-water about them. The girls were merrily splashing along through the puddles in their wooden shoes, carrying their pails on wooden yokes slung over their shoulders, when all of a sudden one of them cried:

"Look there! Look there!"

At that the lassies all stood still, and what should they see in a shallow pool before them, but a gleaming silver-green tail, floundering helplessly and churning up a shining shower of water.

"It's a great fish," cried one of the maids, "a fish, carried in by the flood!"

"It will never get back," said another, "for this pool is standing alone with no outlet to the sea!"

But just as they spoke, the third lass gave a shriek.

"O look, look! It's a mermaid!"

There, as sure as butter and cheese, rising from the water, appeared the dripping head and shoulders of a woman,—a beautiful woman with sea-green hair and the glistening tail of a fish!

The girls stood open-mouthed.

"What a curious thing!" whispered one. "Let's take her to the city."

All this time, the poor mermaid was struggling sadly with her arms to get out of the mud, hoping to reach a place where she could float and make her way back to the sea. It was beautiful where she lived far out on the sapphire waters. Her friends and loved ones were there, sporting with the waves. She must return. She must. But the bevy of Edam lassies surrounded her. Though she protested with all her might, they lifted her in their arms and carried her off to the town.

17

Past quiet, shady canals, by the huge towering Gothic Church, as solid as a fortress, they bore her struggling and straining, to the great Town Hall. And when the Burgomaster heard that a mermaid had been found you may well believe that he came to the Town Hall in a hurry, in as much of a hurry, that is, as his dignity would permit him. And the town-councillors came likewise, and crowds and crowds of people—for Edam was a great city in those days, the water gate to Amsterdam, with twenty-five thousand burghers; and as many of that twenty-five thousand as could walk or run or hobble, came clumping and clattering to see the marvelous wonder cast up for them by the sea.

First they fed the mermaid and treated her very kindly, till they stopped her wild struggling and put her at her ease. Then they set about in proper manner debating what they should do with her.

The Burgomaster was of opinion that a mermaid could not be permitted to remain a mermaid in Edam. A mermaid was a wild, fantastical creature, savoring too much of Fairyland. She had no place in a sober, substantial city like Edam.

18

Now, you must know that the burghers of Edam have little to do with mermaids and giants and fairies. They live in a placid and beautiful country and are content with the world as it is. What need have they to go building castles in the air, or riding the horses of fancy to the moon? Leave it to the poor folk of the barren heath or fen-country to the northward and eastward, in Drente or thereabouts, to run off to Fairyland and have dealings with elves and earthmen and giants. Their own land is poor enough. No wonder at times they must needs run away on the fluttering wings of fancy. Not so with North Holland, ah, no, indeed! North Holland is rich and green and satisfying as it is. No need to fly away from North Holland on a wild goose chase into the clouds! So say the people of Edam. North Holland is the Land-of-Reality, the Land-of-things-as-they-are, the country of markets and black and white cows! And Edam, ah, Edam is the city of cheese, famed to the uttermost ends of the earth for the glories of its cheese. In such a place, pray tell, what room was there for a mermaid?

The Burgomaster gazed upon the coat-of-arms of Edam, hanging

The mermaid is in a costume after the portrait painter, Franz Hals (1580-1666), and the child was suggested by *The Child with a Parrot* by Van Meiereveldt (1567-1641). See page 152.

on the wall before him, and he was well pleased that it was adorned with no griffin or dragon or such-like fantastical monster. It bore the figure of a fine, sleek, fighting steer, with no nonsense whatever about him, and as the Burgomaster looked, he exclaimed with great solemnity:

"We cannot let a mermaid remain a mermaid in Edam. There is only one thing to do. We must make her over into a useful Edam housewife!"

"But,—" cried a very young town-councillor, with a flash of inspiration, "why not take her back and put her in the sea?"

The Burgomaster was shocked. Impressively, he replied:

"Nay, that would be shirking our bounden duty. If we put her in the sea, the poor thing will remain always a mermaid and never be anything better. Since she has been brought to us, we must civilize her and make her like ourselves. We must turn her into a good burgher-vrouw with no absurd nonsense about her."

"But," objected the young town-councillor. "Maybe she wasn't meant to be a good burgher-vrouw. Perhaps it isn't in her nature to be a burgher-vrouw. Perhaps she was meant to be a mermaid and sport in the water. Who are we, that we should try to make her like ourselves? Would it not be best to put her back in the sea?"

But the Burgomaster and the older men frowned sternly on the young fellow and thought him a silly booby who was greatly in need of years and gray hair to bring him wisdom. If he did not know that to be like the burghers of Edam was the height of desirable glories, then he had a great deal to learn, the poor, unfortunate simpleton! Who were they, indeed!

So it was agreed by the city council,—they would make the mermaid over into a proper Edam housewife.

Well, they didn't ask permission of the mermaid, but they dressed her up in robes of the finest fashion then in vogue in the city, and they did their best to cover her long green tail from sight. Every now and then, however, the outlandish thing would show itself below her voluminous petticoats. As to her tell-tale hair with the sea-green sheen like waves flung up by the west-wind, why they hid that beneath a white lace cap. All was of the very best style and quality, you may be sure of that.

And when the mermaid was installed in a good substantial townhouse, the women of the city came by turns to teach her to sew and to spin, and to churn the cheese which is the pride of Edam. They taught her to work, work, work, to save, save, save, and to take such pride in cleanliness, that she could not endure so much as the smallest speck of dirt. They provided her too, with a stout and buxom servant lass, who scrubbed from morning till night,—pots, pans, windows, hearth, door-step, sidewalk, housefront,—yes, even the neat red bricks of the street before the door,—scrub, scrub, scrub! And what would you have? With teaching like this, the mermaid was quite made over. She sewed, she spun, she churned, she looked after her servant lass, and kept her eternally scrubbing.

But sometimes there came memories and a longing upon the mer-maid. She longed for the water again. She longed to play with wind and wave, to fly with the flying-fish, leap with the dolphins. She longed for her little home of shells amid a forest of sea-weed. She longed to lie lazily and sun herself on the rocks. She longed for her old free life among mermen and mermaidens,—that happy, carefree life that had nothing to do with scrubbing, nothing to do with saving, nothing to do with cheese.

Then she would tear off her clothes and wriggle away toward the sea. Aye, at such times it took two strong men to keep her from jumping into the water! It took two strong men to bring her back to the city.

They were very patient with her, very courteous, very kindly, the sturdy burghers of Edam, but they kept unswervingly to their purpose, plodding on and on and on. So, bye-and-bye, they accomplished their end, and crushed all the nonsense out of her. She no longer tried to run away. She became a proper burgher-vrouw, who sewed and spun and churned. Then all the good folk of Edam congratulated themselves.

"We have done a fine work," said they, "to make a mermaid over into a housewife like ourselves." Only sometimes a child, a very young child, would come and sit before the strange woman with a question in his eyes. She knew something he wanted to know, something the burghers of Edam could not tell him. Ah, if she would only speak, she could carry him off to a beautiful land, a free, a glorious, a golden land, where dreams are the only truth.

But alack! the mermaid never spoke. This one thing the burghers of Edam could not accomplish. They could not make her speak Dutch! No, that they could not bring about. They could not make her speak Dutch! And so she never told her secrets to the children.

But one day the Burgomaster came, in condescending glory, to pay an afternoon call and delight his eyes with a sight of the good work done by the burghers, for which he took no small amount of credit to himself. Important, pompous, proud, he stood on the mermaid's threshold.

"Now," he thought, "I shall see how greatly we have improved this poor, silly, flighty creature!"

With that, the servant lass opened the door, and the Burgomaster requested her to lead him to her mistress. And now, from an inner room, the mermaid saw the visitor. Her servant had just scrubbed the floor, which was white as driven snow, and had the mermaid not become a proper Edam housewife? Would any Edam housewife permit a Burgomaster to soil the fresh-scoured planks by trampling them with his boots? She waved a sign to her servant, who straightway picked the Burgomaster up bodily in her arms. Ah, the poor old fellow! How painfully he was astounded! How helplessly he kicked his legs! How wounded was his dignity! She bore him to a chair on the opposite side of the hall. Then, without aye, yes, or no, she set him down, kerplunk, as though he had been a baby; she took off his boots; she put a pair of slippers on his feet; and when she had thus prepared him, she led him across to her mistress. Thus was the Burgomaster rewarded for civilizing a mermaid.

Views through open doorways are particularly characteristic of the Dutch artists, Jan Vermeer (1632-1675), and Peter de Hooch (1630-1681), who painted charming pictures of the interiors of Dutch houses. See page 167.

TEN, TEN'S THE HOUR
Tien Uren, Tien Uren
Ten, strikes the hour
Little girls must scour,
Little boys must fetch the water,
Ten, Ten's the hour.

The costumes in this picture are those of the Island of Marken in the Zuyder Zee. The little boys and girls are dressed just alike until they are six years old, both having long hair and wearing skirts and bonnets. The only difference is that the boys have a little circle sewed on the crown of their bonnets.

The Lady of Stavoren

A Tale from the Province of Friesland

IN DAYS long gone, when the fair green meadows of Friesland had not yet been united to Holland,—for the Frisians were a free folk who once had counts of their own,—Stavoren was one of the mightiest cities in that province. Its towers and spires rose above the Zuyder Zee just at the point where its gray waters open out into the vast reach of the North Sea. Ah! there was a city for you, a city of stately palaces, and splendid public buildings, of rich burghers and strutting nobles.

The reason for all this was, that Stavoren had a beautiful harbor, one of the finest in Friesland. Her ships without number, spread their proud sails to the wind, and rode all the Seven Seas. As time passed, Stavoren became so rich through her merchant vessels, that her burghers began to put golden handles on their doors and golden hinges on their windows. They even went further,—they built before their houses, stoops of pure gold fenced in with golden railings. And then they began to throw out their chests and step very high, and tilt their noses in the air, and point with their fingers across the Zuyder Zee where the lantern in the white cupola of the great Drommedaris Tower kept guard over the fortifications and harbor of Enkhuisen in Holland.

"Over there in Holland, they have no such city as Stavoren," the burghers would say. "Enkhuisen has no citizens who can build stoops of solid gold."

And, thereafter, they threw their chests out further, and tilted their noses higher, and strutted more proudly than ever before.

Now of all the vain and haughty people in Stavoren, none was vainer and haughtier than a certain rich widow. Her husband had been a ship-owner and he had left her so immense a treasure that none knew the whole amount of it. She would pass through the streets with jewels glittering on her long white fingers and all over her splendid robes, and she held her head so high that she scarcely even saw the poorer folk, who bobbed little curtsies as she passed and paid humble respect to such a mighty show. There were few people in the city who did not stand in awe of her.

"Ah," said they, "she is the richest woman in Stavoren!" And alack! poor souls, they knew nothing better than that to say about any living being. They held nothing else of value but riches, riches, riches. Many envied her, many feared her, and a handful strove to outshine her.

One day, a certain ship belonging to this lady, was about to set sail, with a rich cargo, to trade in far ports of the world.

24

"Ha," said the widow to herself. "It is time I got me something to startle these boorish burghers who think themselves so grand. It is time I made them see that their riches are but as a pinch of sand compared to such treasures as mine!"

And she sent off at once in a hurry for the skipper who commanded the vessel. When the honest old fellow stood respectfully before her, she said:

"I order you herewith to search the world and bring back to me in your ship the richest, most beautiful, and precious thing to be bought for gold."

Who knows what she was thinking of? Ivory, perhaps, or peacocks, or diamonds, or gold brocade, or dazzling white ermine fur that should be fit for a king.

"Spare no money or pains," she commanded. "I have ordered your vessel to be loaded with golden coins. Exchange these for the most precious thing in the world."

At such words as these, the old skipper stood for a moment perplexed. How should he know what was the most beautiful and precious thing in the world? But he was a sturdy fellow with a just respect for his own intelligence, so he answered:

"I shall obey you, my lady. I will bring you back the richest, most beautiful and precious thing to be bought for gold."

The very next day his ship set sail and glided out of Stavoren's beautiful harbor, with a line of staring folk waving farewells from the shore.

For many a day thereafter the skipper pondered over the task his mistress had set him. In the rich and magnificent cities of the east, he saw scores of costly and splendid things,—noble work of the goldsmiths, bracelets, rings, sparkling diamonds, embroidered cloths, Byzantine tapestry, gold brocade,—but he was a simple man of the people, and the glitter of things like these had no charm for him. It cast no spell over him whatever. He had not been born in Stavoren. Out on the rich green meadows of Friesland dotted with fat, sleek black and white cattle,— that was where he had lived as a boy, and not in sight of a single golden stoop. Nay! his home had been a thatched cottage, with dairy, barn and cowshed all under the same broad roof. "Work, Work, Work," was the song of life as he knew it, and a happy song it was, altogether in tune with sunshine, and growth and joy. How should such a man value ivory, or peacocks, or diamonds, or gold brocade? They were nothing to him,—light things, vain things, toys, neither precious nor beautiful.

No, in those magnificent eastern cities he could not find the most beautiful and precious thing in the world. Indeed, he had almost given

up hope of ever finding it, when he chanced to sail into the harbor of Dantzig. As he was roaming about the streets of the city, he passed a plain-looking building and saw inside what set his heart leaping for joy, a beautiful hoard of golden treasure,—bushels and bushels of golden wheat.

In all the world what was more beautiful and precious than wheat, —wheat, whence came bread, the very staff of life to men, the gift whereby they renew their strength for the joyous work of the day. Ivory and peacocks and diamonds might vanish from the earth and men be none the worse, but wheat they must have for their comfort and happiness. The skipper's face glowed.

"Where have my wits been all these months?" he said. "Any simple Frisian knows there is nothing in the world more beautiful and precious than wheat. At last I have found what my mistress desires. I will take it home to her."

And he loaded his vessel forthwith, and set sail, again, for Stavoren.

Meanwhile the rich widow had been for months eagerly, impatiently awaiting his return. Day in and day out, she kept fancying what all the people in Stavoren would say when they saw the wondrous treasure her ship was to bring her home.

This picture was suggested by a painting by the Dutch artist, William van de Velde (1633-1707), who loved to paint the sea with high-stemmed Dutch ships sailing over the waves.

"And that fellow, Halbertsma, will stop trying to outshine me when he sees, what I shall have then," she said to herself. "And Mevrouw Cirksena will eat humble pie when she looks at me in my splendor!"

Thus it went. She even boasted far and near of what her ship would bring home.

At length the great day came. Children, running through the streets, shouted in great excitement that the ship was in the harbor. My lady, the Widow, decked herself out in her costliest garments, and off she went to the dock, scarcely able to wait till the ship was made fast to the shore. No one indeed stayed at home that day. All Stavoren hurried off to the wharf,—men, women and children, eagerly flocking to catch a glimpse of the widow's much boasted treasure.

"It will be diamonds as big as eggs," cried some.

"It will be rubies the size of bricks, and turquoises as big as your head!" cried others.

The Captain sprang ashore, his honest face glowing with joy.

"Well," said the lady, her voice trembling with expectancy. "What have you brought me?"

"The finest treasure in all the world."

"Yes, but what is it, what is it?"

"Wheat," answered the Captain with quiet satisfaction. "A ship-load of wheat!"

"Wheat!" stammered the widow, painfully astonished. "You have brought me wheat?"

The costume of this lady is after the Flemish portrait painter, Anthony Van Dyck (1599-1641), for many years the court painter of Charles I of England. See page 157.

"Wheat!" cried the crowd and they all began to snicker. "Wheat! Her wonderful treasure is nothing but common, everyday wheat." Their snicker became a laugh, and their laugh became a sneer, and their sneer became a jeer. The rich woman who had lorded it over them so often, and boasted so haughtily,—she had nothing to show them but wheat, common everyday wheat! Did you ever hear the like?

What a day for my lady, the Widow! All those gibes and jeers from the very men, women and children she had thought to overawe, were like so many pins and needles stuck into her sides. Jab here! Jab there! Ah, well-a-day! What hurts a vain woman more than mockery! When she could control her voice enough to speak, she cried in a rage:

"So! In return for my rich cargo you have brought me back wheat?"

"Yes, Mevrouw!"

"Well, you can take the poor stuff out to the entrance of the harbor and dump it into the sea!"

The Captain was struck dumb. She did not like his precious wheat, his beautiful, useful, golden wheat. He could not understand. To him it was a sacred thing.

"No, no," he cried in great distress. "Don't dump it in the sea!" To throw away food, yes, even a crust or a few crumbs of bread, was that not a monstrous sin? Wheat was God's precious gift to man, and man must treat it with reverence and gratitude. "If you do not care to keep it," he urged, "I pray you, give it to the poor. Many could be fed with that cargo. To throw it into the sea would be so great a sin that it might bring punishment on your head and reduce you to poverty, yes even to dire distress!"

At this the widow grew white with anger. Taking a beautiful ring from her finger, she threw it scornfully into the water and cried:

"Do as you are bid. I fear neither punishment nor distress. As surely as I shall never see this ring again, so surely can I never be poor and in want. Dump the wheat in the sea."

Slowly and sadly, the good Captain turned the vessel about and returned to the entrance of the harbor. Not a voice on shore called him back. Not a voice among all those burghers of Stavoren was raised in protest to save the wheat. One and all, they despised it. They had no respect save for things that glittered. They knew not the value and beauty of simple, homely wheat. They loved only idle show. Had they not built stoops of pure gold with no other purpose than just to show off, to make all the world understand how much greater they were than the good folk of Enkhuisen in Holland across the Zuyder Zee?

It was a sad moment for the Captain,—dumping his wheat in the sea. No more would he serve the Lady of Stavoren. There was an end of that! He must seek a master who understood the real value of things.

And what of the haughty widow? In deepest chagrin, she went back to her home, and scarce did she dare to show her nose out of doors again, for whenever she poked but the tip of it forth, some monkey-faced imp of a boy would gibe, "Say, lady, when is your next treasure-ship coming home?"

Worse than that,—no more than two days later, it chanced that she ordered fish to be served for her dinner. Suddenly, one of her servants came running into her presence, painfully excited, and bearing a fish in his hand. What had he found in its stomach? Her ring! That is what he had found,—her ring that she had cast into the sea! At such a sight, she grew pale, for well she remembered her words: "As surely as I shall never see this ring again, so surely can I never be poor and in want! Dump the wheat in the sea!" And there was her ring come back!

In that self-same hour the Widow received the news that one of her ships had been lost in a storm, and, during the months that followed many such tidings reached her.

And those haughty burghers of Stavoren who thought they should never want . . . !

The very next Spring above the waves of the sea at the entrance to the city's splendid harbor, an ominous green appeared. The wheat, which the burghers had so despised, had taken root and sprung up, only now it grew as a weed and bore no precious fruit, not a single golden grain.

As the days went by, the floating currents of sand which continually sweep around the Zuyder Zee, began to catch in the stalks of wheat and stick there, until they had piled up a sand-bank,—a huge, immovable wall of sand, that closed in Stavoren's harbor. No more could the great ships which had once glided so easily into port, enter the bay at Stavoren. They could not pass that bar. Stavoren was shut in forever.

And so the city lost her harbor, the very source of her wealth. The proud Lady's ships could no longer sail the Seven Seas. Slowly her treasures melted away, her gold, her jewels, her palace; and the wealth of her neighbors likewise vanished into nothing. There were no more golden stoops. Stavoren dwindled and dwindled. With each succeeding year, it grew smaller and less important, till by and by the world forgot it, shut in behind its sandbank.

And so it came about! Where once a haughty city stood, is now but a sleepy village,—a few little gabled, red-roofed houses, half hidden in broad old trees. But everyone remembers still the story of the proud Widow; and the sand bank, which spoiled the harbor, is called to this very day, Vrouwenzand, or Lady's Sand.

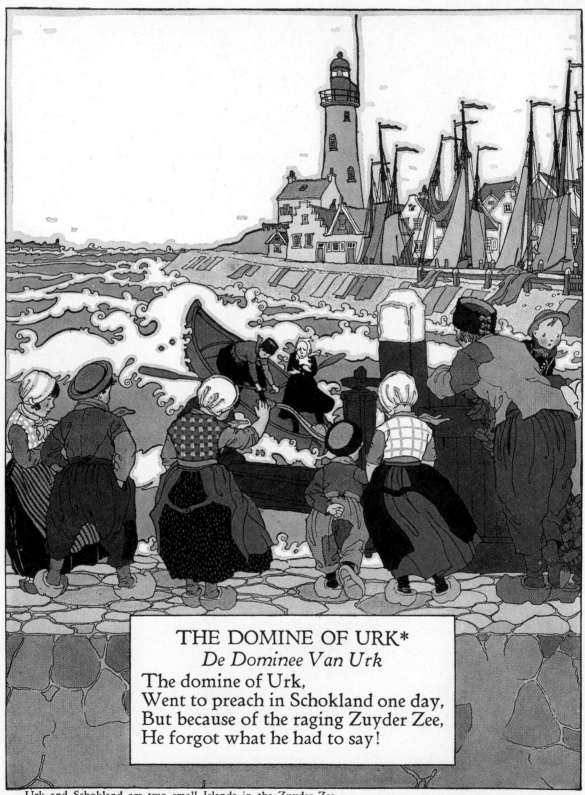

THE DOMINE OF URK*
De Dominee Van Urk

The domine of Urk,
Went to preach in Schokland one day,
But because of the raging Zuyder Zee,
He forgot what he had to say!

* Urk and Schokland are two small Islands in the Zuyder Zee.

30

KLUMPERTY AND HIS WIFIE
Klompertje En Zyn Wyfje

Klumperty and his wifie
Rose early one fine day,
And with their butter and eggs, eggs, eggs,
To market off went they!
They'd gone half way to market,
Half down the dike when thud!
They dropped and broke their eggs, eggs, eggs,
The butter it fell in the mud!
She wept but not for the eggs, eggs, eggs;
'Twas for her shawl, perchance,
Which she had made the day before
Out of Klumperty's Sunday pants.

The costumes in this picture are from Axel in the province of Zeeland.

The Courtship of Hilbert and Japiky

A Tale from the Province of Drente

HILBERT was crossing Ellert's Field, a great sandy heath in Drente. He was whistling and he thought of nothing. From the other side of the field came Japiky, and she, too, thought of nothing. Then they met and both thought the same thing. Hilbert thought:

"That's a nice girl to keep company with."

Japiky thought:

"That's a nice fellow to keep company with."

But they kept on walking so they passed each other, and Japiky sang:

> *"Mother, set my little cap straight;*
> *Tonight my sweetheart comes, you know.*
> *If he comes not, I'll not go after him;*
> *Though he never comes, I'll not go!"*

Singing, Hilbert answered:

> *"Spin, my pretty girl, **spin**!*
> *If you spin not,*
> *Then you'll win not,*
> *Then tonight your sweetheart comes not!"*

Merrily, they slapped their knees, looking back over their shoulders to smile at each other.

"What's your name?" he called to her.

"Albert's Japiky."

"Next Saturday I'm coming to see you."

"I've no objection."

Still they walked on away from each other.

For joy, Hilbert sang the song of his childhood. For joy, Japiky answered him from afar.

Then, though they had walked so very far apart, they sang together, and their voices, thin for distance, blended beautifully one to the other.

After that, they looked back and each saw only a black dot—that was the other who would keep company next Saturday.

Well, on the next Saturday night, Hilbert walked over Ellert's Field to Japiky's house. He had a cake of gingerbread under his arm and everyone knows what that means—he was going a-courting in earnest. When he reached the cottage and knocked at the door, he heard a ripple of laughter inside. Japiky poked her little nose out and said: "Have you any gingerbread?" And everyone knows what that means—she was ready to listen to his courting in earnest.

Hilbert's heart went pit-a-pat for joy.

"Yes," said he, "I've brought the gingerbread."

With that, he went into the house, and there were Japiky's mother and father and six little brothers and sisters all ready in a row to stare at him. They looked him well over, up and down, before and behind. They asked him this and that and the other thing, and when they had made up their minds he was good enough for Japiky, they all went off and crawled into the various holes in the wall where they slept, leaving Hilbert and Japiky quite alone. And everyone knows what that means —it was as good as saying, "Bless you, my children. You have our consent. Marry if you like!"

So Hilbert put his gingerbread down on the table. Words didn't come very readily to his tongue, but he looked at Japiky sweetly with question in his eyes, and what did Japiky do but hurry over and put more peat on the fire to make it blaze up with inviting warmth. And everyone knows what that means, too! She couldn't have said more plainly: "I've a mind to say, 'yes,' to your courting!"

Hilbert was very happy, so he cut the cake, and gave Japiky a piece, and the two sat down by the fire together. Then Hilbert took Japiky's hand and said:

"Japiky, I think you're such a sweet girl. I like you so much. Shall we get married?"

But at that, all of a sudden, Japiky drew her hand away, shook her head pertly and jumped to her feet.

"Keep still with your nonsense!" said she. "There are other young men besides you in the world! I've no mind to settle down yet. I like to keep up the song-and-dance with other young fellows. Perhaps— by-and-by—later on—next year!"

And this she said to try him, looking at him secretly from the corners of her eyes, for no young lassie likes to feel her young man is too soft and yielding. Aye!—that was the time for Hilbert to say: "No non-sense here, my lass! Today is a very good day, and no by-and-by is nearly so good. Either you love me now, and will have me now, or you don't love me now and you'll have me never! And now you say yes or now you say no!" But Hilbert had never in all his life been so firm and determined as that. He was of a disposition as soft and yielding as butter. He never held out for a yes, if anyone else said no more than twice. If a friend had said to him, "Hilbert, go jump in the pond!" he might have said no once, he might have said no twice, but the third time, ten to one, he would have taken a run and a jump and plunged obedi-ently into the water. Such was Hilbert. So when Japiky struck him all of a heap with her sudden "By-and-by," he fell a-hemming and haw-ing and saying, "O Japiky, —!" and "Why, Japiky, —?" and "But, Japiky, —!" and the more he said, "O, Japiky, —!" and "Why, Japiky, —?" and "But, Japiky, —!" the more Japiky bridled her head and grew set in her determination to put off saying yes.

By-and-by, she pushed him to the door.

"Come back next year," said she. "No sooner and no later. Come exactly a year from today, and then, and then," she laughed aloud, "I'll marry you and only you!" With that she gave his nose a mischievous little tweak, pushed him altogether out of the house, and shut the door in his face.

Hilbert was dumbfounded. But what did he do then? Did he push open the door again by the force of his good right arm as any sturdy young lad should have done? Did he walk boldly into the house, take Japiky firmly by the shoulders, bid her stop her nonsense and come to terms on the instant? No, not he! Instead, he sighed, and sighed, and sighed, and then he trudged off obediently through the moonlight, home across the heath.

Now, you may easily guess that Hilbert's work didn't go very well during the year that followed. As the needle of a compass always turns to the north, so Hilbert's face was always turned northward, where Japiky lived across Ellert's Field. Day in and day out, he thought of nothing but Japiky. And so the lad who had once been as jolly and strong a young fellow as any to be found in the whole wide, free, heathlands of Drente, grew pale and languishing like one who lives shut up in the city. No singing and no whistling for him. In his innermost heart there was no other sound but "Japiky, Japiky, Japiky!" and "How long, how long, how long is a year!" One year? One year? Five years, six years that one year seemed to him. But fortunately, even five and six years pass. There came a day—hay, 'twas in the May! when Hilbert set out once more to see Japiky north of the field.

How was Hilbert dressed? Not in his best clothes—you may be sure of that! No! he wore his everyday togs and carried his Sunday suit over one arm. It was dusty out there on the heath. He did not wish to spoil his best clothes as he walked. Said he to himself, "I'll put on my Sunday suit just before I come to Japiky's house!"

For a long time Hilbert walked on in silence. He saw only wide stretches of sandy heath with now and then droves of sheep under the care of a shepherd. By-and-by, he came to a lonely spot—no sheep, no shepherd, no sign of a living thing as far as the eye could see. Suddenly he plunged through a clump of purple heather and came out on the top of a hill. Below him, lay a hollow, a little bowl-shaped hollow. And what did he see there? This is what he saw—hundreds of little elves swarming in the sunlight! Some lay on their backs and kicked up their heels; others stamped with their feet on the ground; the rest ran continually back and forth, helter-skelter, helter-skelter. All was stir and turmoil and motion. Each one of these queer little men wore a green jacket, green trousers, and wooden shoes. They all had gray beards and tiny pipes, from which they blew clouds of smoke in the air.

All at once one of these dwarfs spied Hilbert up there above them. He nudged the one next him, and this one in turned nudged the one next him. In a twinkling they were all looking up at Hilbert. Then such a buzzing and whispering as began at once among them! For many years they had met on that lonely spot in peace, and no human being had ever discovered them. But now—here was a man who had found out their secret meeting place! If each one had only had nothing to trouble his conscience, they might not have minded, but elves, alack, are like humans, sometimes good and sometimes bad. Many had done useful work for the farmers round about—had swept the floors in the homes, washed the linen, and built the fires; they had baked and scrubbed and ironed and washed and ploughed and reaped. But others had played

naughty tricks. They had spoiled the butter, drunk the milk of the cows, loosened the rope that tied the goat, and hidden the wooden shoes. Those who had played such pranks were afraid. They deserved nothing good, and they knew it, nothing good at all. The very naughtiest elf was so greatly afraid, that he ran and hid behind a rock and dared not show his face, nor so much as his little finger.

Well, you must know that Hilbert was not much at ease himself. Although the dwarfs were so very small, he thought that all together they could cause him a lot of trouble. He felt like going back home and he hesitated weakly. He dared not stride boldly through them. But as he lingered, the little men began to smell the haunch of ham and the bottle of gin he had brought along for refreshment. Um! and ah! they smelt very good. So, by-and-by the desire of the earthmen to have that ham overcame their fear of Hilbert! The eldest of all, who wore the longest beard, and smoked the biggest pipe, came forward with a grin.

"What are you doing here?" he asked, "and will you not sit down and share your dinner with us?"

Taking courage from this friendliness, Hilbert told the whole story of how he was off to Japiky's.

"But," said the eldest dwarf. "Stay and make merry with us this afternoon. You'll have plenty of time after that to get to the girl before midnight."

"Thank you very kindly," said Hilbert, "but, you see, I must also have time to change my clothes, for I'm wearing my everyday suit."

"O come, come," urged the dwarf. "Stay with us. You'll never be sorry!"

Now Hilbert knew perfectly well that he ought not to linger. No dilly-dallying or shilly-shallying if he wished to reach Japiky's on time. But whenever he said no, the elves kept on urging and teasing, for they grew ever greedier to taste that savory ham. So by-and-by, Hilbert hadn't the courage to hold out any longer. He said, "Very well!" Then he sat himself down on the ground and took out his ham and his bottle.

At this, you may well believe, the elves came crowding and swarming about him. Dozens climbed on his knees or sat in rows on his shoulders. They ate, they drank, they smacked their lips; and then they fell a-dancing. Hand in hand they danced all except that naughtiest dwarf who had hid behind a rock. He was not dancing, and he was not merry, the ugly little fellow! He was angry and envious, and, because of the tricks he had played on humans, he had reason to be afraid. At last, he grew so eager for the sweet smelling food and drink, that he poked just the tip of his nose out of his hole. Thus he saw the bottle lying near Hilbert. Carefully, on his hands and knees, he began to wriggle toward it. Every once in a while he lay still for a moment, like a caterpillar, finding a leaf in its way. He was afraid that Hilbert would thrash him if he turned his head and saw him. When he reached the bottle, he snatched it and put it to his lips. Just then Hilbert spied him, and burst into laughter.

"There is nothing left there," he said. And right he was. There wasn't the tiniest drop to be squeezed or coaxed from the bottle, and

worse still, near by on the ground, lay the polished bone of the ham—not a snitch, not a single snitch of the juicy meat remained. Hilbert laughed again at the little man's impotent anger. This made the elf fairly rage. He wrinkled his forehead and shook his fist.

"I'll get you sometime for this, you slow-witted booby!" he cried.

But Hilbert laughed the louder, and the next moment he had forgotten the mean little dwarf entirely. He looked on smiling for hours while the elves were skipping and dancing around him. Not till the very last minute, when time was barely left to reach Japiky's by midnight, did the silly fellow break away and bid farewell to the earthmen.

As he made off from the hollow, the ugly little dwarf peeped out from his hole and saw which road he was taking. Then he followed him like a shadow. When Hilbert went slower, the dwarf ducked down in some furrow, or hid behind the shrubby purple heather, but when Hilbert went faster, he ran again and caught up with him.

Now Hilbert looked at his watch and sighed. He had stayed much too long with the elves. He would certainly have to hurry. And he had to change his clothes, besides! At thought of that, Hilbert walked so fast that the elf could barely keep up with him. Often he had to take little jumps and fairly fly through the air, so as not to lose any ground.

By-and-by, Hilbert entered an inn.

"Now, what does he mean to do there," thought the dwarf and he hastened to peep through the window. This is what he saw. He saw that Hilbert took off his everyday clothes and was about to put on his Sunday suit. But just at that moment, when the lad stood there clad in nothing but his poor little undershift, the ill-natured dwarf spoke a magic formula: "Hocus pocus, mumbo jumbo!" And in a twinkling what happened? Sunday coat, Sunday breeches and Sunday vest all flipped out of Hilbert's hands and flew out of the door as if they had wings!

Hilbert cried out in alarm, and hurried after the runaways. He thought the wind must have carried them off and a little chase would recover them. But as he ran, those clothes fluttered high in the air, far higher than himself, the arms of the coat flying one way, the legs of the trousers another! He jumped, he leaped to catch them. All was in vain. They seemed to be alive, flipping out of his reach to mock him.

Such a storm as that he had never known—the wind blew only where his clothes flew! Elsewhere not a leaf quivered, not a blade of grass stirred. Only that coat, those trousers, that vest, went flying down the road!

It was awful! It was terrible, to be off for one's wedding in an undershift, with one's everyday clothes left behind at the inn, and one's Sunday suit running away like mad. There was only one comfort left to poor Hilbert. The clothes seemed to be going in the direction of

Japiky's house. If they had flown off the other way he would have been beside himself, for then he must surely have been too late for the wedding. Now, at least, there was still a chance that he might reach Japiky, before the clock struck twelve.

A wild chase it was! All unknown to Hilbert, the dwarf climbed up his leg and held on with both hands. Otherwise he could not have kept up with him. Over roads and no roads plunged Hilbert, over ditches, over trenches, over hedges. It was like a dream, but it was no dream! Alack! it was mocking reality! His clothes ever ran before him!

Not till they reached Japiky's very front door did the runaways stop. There they dropped down in a heap! Hilbert plunged toward them panting. It was his last and only chance. But from under his very grasp they flew up high above the house and floated a moment in the air. Then they dived down the chimney. Hilbert groaned and ran to the window to press his face against the pane. Inside he saw his Japiky! Ah, too truly was she carrying out her desire to keep up the song-and-dance with other young fellows, for she had three beaux beside her and all were making merry. As they sat there together before the hearth, the clock struck the fatal hour of twelve. On the very first stroke, down the chimney, kerplunk, fell Hilbert's clothes. There they lay humped up mid the ashes like a limp rag-doll copy of Hilbert! But with the last hoarse stroke, the elf's magic power vanished. He jumped down from Hilbert's leg and ran away with a laugh. Then the silly lad knew who had played the trick and the price he had paid for dallying.

What was there after that to do, as Hilbert stood there shivering, but to call to the people in the house and beg them to hand him his clothes? And when they peeped forth and saw him,—Japiky and her three merry beaux,—what laughter! what jeers! Out in the dark he dressed and got ready to hear his sentence. It was no very kind sentence either.

Why did he come so late, asked Japiky.

Then he should not have stopped at the elves' place!

Why was his suit so dusty?

Then he should have run faster and caught it.

And would she still be willing to marry him?

Yes, but not this year! Next year he must come back on the very same day of the month, no sooner and no later, and he must get there before midnight. For she thought he was a pretty nice fellow—and perhaps,—next year,—by-and-by,—maybe,——!

But what happened next year is another story, and how much longer Hilbert let Japiky keep him waiting, I haven't the least idea.

A WIND MILL
Four old, old women,—
They never could catch each other.
Each ran as fast as the others ran,—
Guess, guess if you can.

These costumes are from the fishing village of Volendam on the edge of the Zuyder Zee.

IT'S RAINING, IT'S GAINING
Het Regent, Het Zegent

It's raining, it's gaining,
The tiles are getting wet,—
There came along three farmers' wives,
And down they sit, sat, set!

This picture shows an ancient square called the Balans, in the old town of Middleburg, province of Zeeland.

41

Abel Stok's Difficult Task

A Tale from the Province of Groningen

BEFORE times long past, it happened in the province of Groningen, that all the towns, canals, ponds and bridges had been given names except two villages and one "till," and if you don't know what a "till" is, possess yourself in patience. By-and-by you shall hear. Now this is a serious matter to have two nameless villages, and one miserable, nameless "till." All the professors of the University, all the lawyers of the province, all the farmers of the land, who are far more clever than either professors or lawyers, set their wits to work to find the names that were lacking. But they racked their brains in vain. They could not find a name. Then a man from Delfzyl said:

"Let us appoint a committee to look into this question."

Of course if the man of Delfzyl proposed such a thing, the men from Appingedam would oppose it. That is the way it goes between these two towns. Whatever is Yea to one is Nay to the other. But the Appingedammers lost out against a majority of votes and the committee was formed in right and proper manner. They met in a certain coffee house and drank their Groningen beer. In spite of all this, however, they could not decide the matter. Many names were proposed but not one was accepted. They considered, they argued, they cogitated; they mused, they discussed, they deliberated. And still, after all, they could not agree on a name.

Now one summer day, when the wisemen of the council were all thus gathered together, a stranger entered the inn, unannounced, a very strange man indeed. He was tall and thin, thin of leg, thin of arm, thin of body and head. He was large of nose, huge of mouth, enormous of ears, and his long mustache hung down in carefully twisted points. As he took a seat among the wise men, everyone slightly frowned. But the stranger sweetly said: "I notice that you gentlemen cannot solve a difficult problem," and then they all looked at him in surprise, as a group of learned men will sometimes look at a humble poet. They grumbled a little, scraped their throats, scratched behind their ears, said "yes, yes—, yes, yes—," and "so, so—, so so,—!" But the president decided the matter boldly. Moving his chair close to the stranger's, he said:

"I beg your pardon, but do you know what we are trying to find?"

"Certainly, certainly!"

"And what is your name, if I may ask?"

"Abel Stok!"

"Abel—Abel—a good name!" cried the members of the committee. "Let us try him. If it does not help us, it cannot harm us either!"

"Well, Mr. Abel Stok," asked the president politely, "what is your proposition?"

"Mr. President! Gentlemen!" said Abel Stok. "I move that we have a race in pole-vaulting, near one of the places that has no name. He who jumps the farthest, may name the two villages and the bridge."

"It is not a bridge, it is a 'till'!" said the president, and he was right. For a bridge that turns or lifts up to let boats go by is a bridge, but a fixed bridge is a "till," just as a boat is a boat, but a towboat is a "snik." All nodded their approval. In cases like this, it is well to start out right, calling things carefully by their correct and proper names.

Well, it was a good proposition that Abel had made. "For is not pole-vaulting a popular sport in our land," cried the wisemen, "and do not the very boys carry poles to school in order to hop across the little canals that bar their paths through the meadow?"

When the great day of the contest came, many a Groninger vaulted. They went out to the canal that ran through one of the nameless villages, they put their poles in the water and leapt across in turn. There could be seen vaulting, learned, fat doctors with spectacles on their noses, skinny schoolmasters, who taught the A, B, C's on other days. Without distinction as to religion, there vaulted Catholics, and Israelites; Dutch Reformed, Lutherans and Walloons; Reformed A's and Reformed B's; aye, Baptists and Jansenists, also. Without distinction as to rank, scholars, with or without a doctor's title, vaulted beside a street cleaner. Many a person, not used to vaulting, slid down the pole, and fell plump! into the water. It was a great adventure. The few who reached the other side were rewarded with mighty applause, with shouts and clapping of hands. Never before or after in our country have people vaulted with so much ambition, only for the honor.

Finally Abel's turn came. He put the pole down into the water, and there he flew up above the treetops, up and up, and up. Aye, he flew so high that he neared the clouds! He rose higher still; he became nothing but a little speck in the blue; he got above the clouds and then he could not be seen at all. He vanished altogether.

Where had Abel gone?

He deserved the prize, and no doubt whatever about it, but still he had flown so very high! Many of the onlookers muttered:

"Never shall we see that MENSCHE WEER," which is to say: "Never shall we see that Man Again!"

And their neighbors answered them:

"You are right,—never shall we see that MENSCHE WEER!"

It was fifteen minutes that Abel was lost in the clouds, but at the end of that time, the little black speck appeared again in the sky. Gradually it grew larger and larger, till one could make out it was Abel dropping gracefully back to earth. When his feet were once more on solid ground, Abel ran toward the spot where his admirers awaited him. Gladly they shouted:

"Yes, yes, there is that MENSCHE WEER!"

The President of the Committee, himself, met Abel, rose up on his toes and patted him on the shoulder.

"Well, friend Stok, you have won the race! Have you found a name for us?"

"I have just heard a very proper name," said the vaulter, smiling and modest, "MENSEWEER."

"Yes, yes," exclaimed many enthusiastically, "MENSINGEWEER! MENSINGEWEER!"

And to this very day Mensingeweer is the name of that village.

But though Abel Stok had succeeded so well, this was not the only difficult task which was given him to perform. There still remained a "till" and a village that were nameless.

"You know," said the president after an impressive silence, "that now you may think of two more names, one for the other village, and one for the 'till'!"

"It won't be my fault if they don't get good names," cried Abel, and with these words he departed.

Soon after, he reached the second town without a name. The inhabitants stood sadly together, yes, shivering like trees in autumn.

"Why are you so sad?" asked Abel.

He did not immediately receive an answer, but at last a woman took courage, and said with a dull voice:

"Stranger, whosoever you are, hear our tale of woe. We are a village without a name!"

"Oh, is that all? Wait a moment, and I shall think of a name for you!" cried Abel, and no sooner had he spoken the words, than a baker came out of his shop and blew THE HORN. It was his way of announcing that he had just taken his fresh German loaves from the oven. Abel Stok jumped high.

"Burghers!" he said, as soon as he came down to earth. "From now on your village also has a name. It shall be called THE HORN!"

Never again have people enjoyed their bread so much as those burghers did that day. Abel Stok, too, satisfied his hunger; the school children sang a song in his honor, and thereupon he departed.

Now the vaulter faced only the "till" that did not have a name. Musingly, he looked into the water and shook his head. That was a more difficult task,—aye, here was a problem, indeed. How was he to distinguish this bridge from every other bridge that he had seen in his life. The same little wavelets hastened by or beat against the canal banks; the same windmills stood near, the same black and white cows were grazing in the same green pastures around it. Nothing different here to suggest a name. Abel was thinking of leaving it to someone else to find a name for the till, when an idea suddenly struck him.

"Why," he thought, "shall I not name this fixed bridge after myself? Have I not became a famous man, a famous man in Groningen?"

And the end of the story is this. Today if you come to the province of Groningen, you must not fail to take a walk out to ABELSTOKSTERTILL. It is the correct thing to do. The Groninger in Amsterdam honors the great artist, Rembrandt, by visiting Rembrandt Place, and pays homage to the greatest of Dutch poets, Vondel, by going to Vondel Park. So why should the visitor to Groningen not visit Abelstoksterstill. We must honor our great men! And Abel Stok is Groningen's hero!

AUNTY LUCE
Aunty Luce
Sat on a goose.
"Flop!" said the goose,
And away flew Aunty Luce!

TANTE NANS
Tante Nans
Zat op een gans.
"Wip!" zei de gans,
En weg vloog Tante Nans!

The old lady in this picture has two bonnets, a straw one on top of her lace cap.

The Giants and the Dwarfs

A Tale from the Veluwe (Bad Land) of the Province of Gelderland

ONCE upon a time there came to the high sandy hills of the Veluwe, three young giants. Where they came from no one knows. They lived without care, and were always happy and merry.

When they were romping and ran after each other over the hills, the ground trembled under their feet.

Now the dwarfs, who lived in the earth, were afraid and listened, quaking, to the noise.

"The great boobies will knock down our hills," they cried. "They will make the earth cave in."

In great distress, the little men peeped here and there through the bushes, but when one of the young giants came running in their direction, the dwarfs ran off as fast as they could, and crawled down into their holes.

Evenings, when the boisterous fellows were tired, they laid themselves down to sleep, side by side, against the hill-slope, and then they began to snore. Indeed, they snored so loud that the dwarfs in the hill below could not sleep a wink all night.

Still, they were not naughty nor malicious giants,—no, not at all; for often while they were sleeping, a smile crept over their beautiful young giants' faces. Well, this can only happen when one is good and carefree.

The next day the game started anew. They chased the wolves, drove them into the wolves' forest and locked them up in it. Or they caught a bear and made him dance; but the eldest of the brothers, who had the kindest heart, freed the wolves and the bear. He could not endure that anything should be unhappy merely to give them pleasure. So they romped and played all day.

That evening, hand in hand, they returned to the big hill.

The sun was just going down and the two younger brothers immediately fell asleep; but the eldest of the three sat a long time watching the wonderful colors in the sky, and he could not explain the strange flood of feeling which suddenly came over him.

Until that evening he had accepted everything as it was. He had never stopped to think what was beautiful, what was ugly; but now he felt in his heart an unknown bliss. He had always known that the sun-god every night rode away through the far wide gates of Asgard; but to him it was as if he had seen the golden glory, the crimson splendor of the sunset this night for the very first time in his life.

From the other side now came approaching the silent mist spirits. They rose slowly around the hill, but none came up to the spot where he was sitting.

When the big eye of night looked down above the distant woods, it saw him still on the hill; but at last he stretched himself beside his brothers and soon was snoring as loudly as they.

And again the dwarfs did not sleep a wink.

The third day, when the giants awoke, they looked around and saw that from the point where they stood, they could see far and wide, over all the country round about.

There lay the woods, the endless heath, and the sandy hills. Farther up were the rivers and lakes, gleaming like bright blue eyes. It was a beautiful, lonely place, the vast wide stretch of the Veluwe. Few houses, few villages! Only way off there to the northward on the Zuyder Zee were some clusters of fishermen's huts and to eastward the little towns and villages planted in the fertile soil along the Yssel River.

The oldest giant spoke to the other two:

"This is a beautiful country," said he. "Let us settle here and build a hut."

The others agreed with him and they decided to start the work at once.

All day long they hauled trees and rocks and squares of sod which they cut from the heath. They pulled up four sturdy oaks by the roots and placed them as poles at the corners of the house. Between these the walls were made of firs and grassy sods.

With an oaken club the giants rammed the trees into the ground, to the great dismay of the dwarf people. In every blow, the little folk heard the powerful expression of a giant's determination and then the tree sank a foot deeper in the ground.

When evening came, their home was ready and they built their first fire on the hearth.

That night again the dwarfs did not sleep a wink; but they assem-

bled, hundreds of them, out on the heath in the moonlight, and talked the matter over.

Now the dwarfs build their homes far down in the earth. There they have many tunnels and rooms, kitchens and parlors, and everything nice. Often people have tried to find the entrances to their houses, but quite in vain. They have never been able to find them. Some say the dwarfs enter the earth through rabbit holes hidden somewhere in a pit or under the heather. Others declare they use magic words which can turn a stone into a door, or make a door, a stone. However that may be, the dwarfs were not at all pleased at having giants walking above them. They are a timorous little folk. Don't you believe that dwarfs will ever come out in the open and stand up to any danger. Not they, no indeed! They play their pranks and tricks when no one is about, but if others more powerful than they, appear, the little folk run away and hide and only oppose them in secret.

Now when the dwarfs had gathered together, one of the most important, who spoke very well, and liked to hear himself talk, climbed up on a rock and addressed the others.

"Dear friends," he said. "Our hills are visited by a real plague. If we do not drive these giants away, we shall not be able to live here. They walk so awkwardly that our houses almost fall in. They snore so noisily that we cannot sleep a single night. At this very moment my words are out-voiced by the hideous racket they are making. There is only one thing to do. We must destroy the house they have built."

Then the dwarfs wagged their heads very wisely and agreed with the speaker. There was only one little dwarf woman who raised her voice modestly and spoke in behalf of the giants:

"But these giants are jolly fellows," she said. "I'm sure they mean no harm. Why should we fear them merely because they are bigger than we? If we would but go and set the matter frankly before them, I believe they would keep off those hills beneath which we live, and all of us might dwell peacefully here on the Bad Land, together."

At that, O me and O my, there was an outcry among the dwarfs. What does a woman know of such matters? Who does she think she is to raise her voice in a council of men! The dwarf woman's husband was greatly ashamed of his wife, and he sent her off packing that very instant.

"Go home and mind the kitchen," he scolded, "but don't stand there babbling about things you don't understand."

And so the matter was decided.

The dwarfs toiled and labored all night long and tried to dig up the trees that supported the house; but by the next morning they had dragged away only a couple of sods from the roof, and had dug nothing at all but a few little holes around the corner poles.

When the giants got up the next day, they saw these holes. But all they said to each other was:

"There seem to be many rabbits hereabouts."

Then one of them gave a single stamp with his heel and filled the holes up solid, and the other took the two sods in one hand and put them again on the roof.

That night, when the sun had set, the dwarf people again assembled by moonlight, and the little man who knew-it-all, once more stood on a rock and spoke to the swarming crowd.

"Last night," he said, "we tried to break down the house of the giants; but it is put together so tight and strong, that we could never destroy it. What we tear down in a whole long night, they build up in but one little moment. Nevertheless, if we cannot match them in strength, and power, this we can do,—we can tease them, and annoy them, and thwart them in all kinds of little ways, till we make life so disagreeable that they have to run away. For this is certain, my friends, little men understand the use of little weapons, teasing, annoying, stinging!"

But here the voice of the speaker was quite drowned out by that of another dwarf, who had stood in the rear and kept on shouting right along:

"I know a remedy, a good remedy, a satisfactory remedy!

"Out with it, speak up, what is it?" shouted all.

"We shall steal some fire from their hearth tonight," said the dwarf, "and with it we shall set the house on fire!"

The mass cheered:

"Yes, yes, we must set the house on fire, then we shall be delivered of this nuisance."

"But how do we get in," asked one of the calmest dwarfs.

"Why, we'll dig a tunnel under the house to the hearth," answered another.

Then they all scampered from the platform to the hill to start their work immediately.

They dug and dug, but the three young giants, who were sleeping above them, carefree, snored so loudly, that with every breath, they knocked down pieces of earth which choked the tunnel so the dwarfs had to begin once more and dig all over again. Finally no one had courage left to continue the work. One and all, they ran away.

The next day the giants said to each other:

"There seem to be moles under the house,—there is a tunnel here. We shall put some rocks on the floor and stamp the dirt around them."

That night the three giants sat on the stone floor around the hearth. The fire was burning merrily and they sat up late to talk about their plans,—they would plant trees, they would sow rye and potatoes and buckwheat and such other products as grow upon sand. Why call these hills the "Bad Lands?" If one but used his wits and was willing to work, he could raise good crops in the sand!

The door stood ajar, and outside in the big still night, stood the dwarf folk and peeped in. While they were standing there, they were forced to admire the strong house and the three good looking young giants; but their dwarf souls expressed this admiration in a strange and peculiar manner.

"Now, look at this awkward house," said one.

"Such rude rafters," said another.

"And such a hard floor," spoke a third.

"What ugly, stupid monsters these giants are," cried a fourth. "They know nothing whatever about how to build a house. We could teach them that. Who ever builds a home above the ground? It is plain that the storm spirits will upset it. Such an ugly, gross thing sticks out above all and mars the landscape. We must wipe it out as soon as we are able."

"I think it's a very nice house," piped up the little dwarf woman, but her husband shut her up in a hurry and sent her off to the kitchen more quickly than before.

The giants did not notice anything of what was going on outside,— they were all wrapped up in their plans, their big plans for sowing and building. But when they went to bed, alack! They forgot to lock their door.

The youngest giant woke up first. It was the smell of burning that roused him from his sleep, and when he looked around, the whole room was full of smoke about him! Flames were everywhere.

Quickly he roused his brothers. Just in time and not a moment to spare! They ran from the house, and in an instant behind them the heavy rafters which held the roof fell down crash to the earth.

Bewildered, the brothers watched the destruction of the good, solid house, which they had built with such endeavor.

Behind every bush, dwarfs sat giggling, and on the plain they danced in a big circle around the burning house. But the three great giants were far too big to see them. Speechless, they stared at the high flaming fire.

"We must have forgotten to lock the door yesterday," said the second brother at last. Aye, those giants blamed themselves when evil came

upon them. Leave it to the dwarf-folk to look about and find fault with someone else. "I think the wind has blown some sparks from our hearth."

"From now on we must lock the door carefully," said the oldest giant.

"First we must have a door," said the second brother.

"Tomorrow we shall start to build again," they cried, almost in one breath, "and then we shall build not one house, but three! If one house burns down, we shall still have two left whole."

Fright and dejection were gone. Before sunrise they had started again pulling up trees and cutting out sod.

With hatred in their hearts, the dwarfs had to look on. And lo, a new building went up, while the ashes of the old one had not yet left off smoking.

In the strokes of the giants' clubs the little folk heard again determination and courage, strength and power and joy. That evening, another, still more solid and beautiful house was ready for the giants.

Within a week there stood three houses like that.

And at night the doors were bolted.

When all this was ready, the giants began to spade the ground and to sow rye, and while they were working, they sang. Merrily they sang.

The dwarfs put insects and weeds in the fields. But the three brothers did not complain. They pulled the weeds, they planted their grain still deeper in the earth, and they never left off singing.

One day when they had little to do, they went to the forest and got some young beech trees, which they planted on top of the hill to protect their home-steads against the strong winds from the west.

Then the dwarfs dug under the trees and cut the tiny roots. But if one little tree died, what did the giants do? They planted two in its place. Slowly those trees began to grow, and because they must conquer such difficulties, they became exceedingly strong. Soon the roots were so tough, that the dwarfs could not cut them through with their knives.

And so in the end, what happened? What could be done against beings who would not be teased, or annoyed, who always did better work for every apparent failure? What could be done against beings, who built three houses when one was burned down, and planted three trees when one was destroyed?

The dwarfs were obliged to give in. They had to accommodate themselves to the presence of the giants, as they should have done long before. Only, instead of asking the giants to move away from their hills, as they might have done in the beginning, it was they, the dwarfs, who must move. They had to build their homes where the giants would not disturb them.

On summer evenings the oldest giant often sat at the door of his house, and looked west, where the sun-god drove his golden wagon through Asgard's open gates, while his thoughts went back to that evening, when he saw it for the first time, while his brothers were sleeping so peacefully; to the time when they locked the wolves in the forest, made the bear dance, and built the first house on the heath.

Years went by. The giants cultivated the fields and the trees. The fields became more fertile and the trees grew slowly, but became strong and hardy, their roots shooting deep into the earth.

More than once the storm spirits tried to upset them.

On wild, dark nights they came in big, savage troops. They pulled on the sturdy trunks, attacked with their black claws the leafy tops and yelled out their devilish discords. But the next day there would be only some delicate leaves lying on the ground. The trees themselves stood stronger, stronger than before.

Many years later, when people came to this place, they found here well cultivated land and three quiet, moss-grown houses. So they called the place, Three.

Now the trees are standing there like protecting watchmen. Their roots grow far down into the earth, and their towering heads are a fixed landmark to guide the skippers far out on the Zuyder Zee.

They are standing there, high and immense, and nothing prevails against them. With reason, too, for they were planted by giants.

BIM, BAM, BEGGS
Bim, Bam, Beieren

Bim, bam, beggs,
The farmer won't eat eggs;
He'll eat, if he can,
Ham in the pan,
And that makes fat our farmer man!

HANSY KNIPPERDOLLETY
Hansje Knipperdolletje

Hansy Knipperdollety
Sat on the dike one day;
He scratched his little noodle,
And his cap it blew away!

I CROSSED THE RIVER MAAS, LARIDAAS

Ik Voer Laatst Over de Maas, Laridaas

I crossed the river Maas, laridaas,
With Uncle Johnny Klontery,—
For cheese we went across!
While I was crossing o'er, laridore,
The roosters all were crowing,
And the day was dawning bright,
And the maid she swept the house, laridouse,
What found she in her broomikin?
A penny and a cross!

This picture was suggested by a view across the Maas to Dordrecht, painted by Albert Cuyp (1605-1691), a Dutch painter of landscapes, who loved to paint rich meadows and black and white cows browsing in the sunshine. The figures are after Gerard Ter Borch (1617-1681), a painter of men and women of the upper classes.

The Cat's Cup of Vlaardingen

A Tale from the Province of South Holland

AT THE mouth of the river Maas, half way between the Hook of Holland and Rotterdam, lies the quaint old city of Vlaardingen, which, for centuries, has been sending its fishermen after cod and herring far out into the wind-swept waters of the North Sea.

Now it chanced one day that a couple of boys who were going in swimming, stood near the Vlaardingen Locks at daybreak. The old war between night and morning was just beginning. The sun sent his legions forth. Look, the brilliant spies came creeping. Stealthily they glided through the cracks in the night. After them, the bold young knights pressed onward in gleaming armor, hurling long lances of light into the heavy darkness.

To the boys, shivering with cold, the day seemed like every other day. They wished that they had waited until the sun had defeated the darkness and gained full sway over the earth.

"Look, a ship," cried one of them suddenly.

"Where, where? Boy, you're dreaming."

"One, two, three masts."

"I don't see a thing."

"Are you blind?" He pointed with his finger.

From the dark distance, in the half light of the dawn, the ship came, gliding,—thin, unearthly like mist. The two boys stared with all their eyes. It was weird. It was ghostly,—a phantom. So slowly approached the three-master, that dawn had made way for the day, when the ship came to anchor in the harbor. And still the boys stood motionless.

"There are hardly any men on deck,—those are women," they cried. "And they are dressed in sail-cloth."

"The one at the rudder is a man. B-r-r, what long moustaches he has!"

"What strange eyes he has. See him look at us now!"

"The women folk do nothing but talk. Hear them rattle and cackle! Nobody works on board."

"How high the ship lies. Does she carry no cargo at all!"

So strange was the sight, that the boys were soon joined by a throng of people crowding the line of the shore. Carpenters, sail-makers, rope-makers, barrel-makers, all who had any trade in the ancient city of Vlaardingen came hurrying to the spot. They asked:

"What kind of a ship is that?" Then they said:

"Such a ship we have never seen before in the city of Vlaardingen."

And yet, not one among them could say in what respect the ship differed from other vessels. They could only whisper that no such ship had ever been seen by man unless it were in a dream. In fact, the Locks did not look like Locks; even the crowd of people themselves in the light of this strange new arrival, looked misty and unreal, like people in a dream. After they had seen the ship, nobody was surprised that women reigned on the deck.

"Look at those women, shoving and pushing each other to get to the shore," they cried. "Is no one going to stay on board?"

One and all, the crew jumped to land, the man at the helm and the sailors; but as soon as they had set their feet on the sand, their human forms vanished. The sailors became cats, slender and supple and mewing; the helmsman turned into a fat tom-cat with large, round, bright, green eyes.

Startled at such a sight, the townspeople all ran away as fast as their legs would carry them. Even the street boys had not the courage to linger.

Off went the cats, racing and chasing and leaping, the big tom-cat in the lead.

"Sss—mew—mew." Suddenly they stopped.

Behind them, in the harbor, their ship grew small, smaller and smaller, till its hull became a nutshell, its three masts dwindled into three pins with tiny doll's kerchiefs for sails, and its rudder turned into a pin head. Bounce! A little kitten, young and quick, went springing back to the harbor. Clawing and scratching, she got the toy-ship out of the water. With her little paws she dug a hole in the sand and buried the tiny shell. Mew——mew! And back once more to her friends.

Then the wild chase started again. The weird band visited every street in the little old town, round about the church and the handsome old town hall, round and round, a giddy whirl. They did not stop once, no, not for an instant. All the good folk of the city ran into their houses and shut and bolted their doors. What did they want with such a crew? Yea, though it was broad day-light, they left off their work on sails, and boats, on barrels and ropes, and fishing nets, and ran away to their homes. Even the respectable tabby-cats, who sunned themselves, day in and day out, on Vlaardingen's peaceful doorsteps, would have nothing to do with creatures who behaved themselves like these. Nay, they crept inside four walls and refused to show the strangers so much as the tips of their whiskers. These were no kin of respectable cats and no doubt, whatever, about it!

The fat helmsman ran like mad. Scarcely could the smaller cats

keep up the pace he set. Then suddenly he stopped, and his comrades came crowding around him.

Between his paws, the great cat held a silver goblet. From this he drank slowly, and when he had finished, he graciously handed the cup to his sweetheart who stood beside him. At that a little kitten humped up her back for envy. "Yah-psg!" She snarled and put her claws defiantly on the goblet, looking up at the tom-cat with great, sparkling, yellow eyes, that were both soft and menacing.

"R-r-r, R-r-r," purred the Sultan's sweetheart, soothingly. It was as though she had said she would give the cup to the kitten the moment

she had finished; but when she had had her drink, it was no such thing she did. She passed the cup over the kitten's head and on to a friend of hers, with whom she had danced paw-in-paw.

"Yah-psg," snarled the little kitten again, humping her back still higher. And so it went with that crazy crew,—snarlings and purrings, —nothing nice. When they had all had a turn at the cup they fell to dancing,—swinging, swaying round and round with never a bar of music.

By-and-by a cart came down the road. It was filled with sturdy

farmers. The cats heard the rattle of the wheels and stopped their giddy prancing.

Nearer came the cart. The driver whipped his horses—he must be sure to get to Delft before the market began. It was little use to hide in the house when evils like this presented themselves,—so said the driver's comrades. The day's work must be done. Aye, 'twas better to go forth and boldly face the danger.

"Get up," hollered the driver to make the horses go faster. The hoofs beat on the pavement till the red sparks flew about.

Suddenly there stood the cats barring the road. The horses reared; they threw their heads up wildly; their eyes were white and crazy.

"To the side, cats."

But the cats, with the tom-cat in the center, swayed to and fro; then they straightened up, paw took paw, and the weird dance without a fiddler once again began. The two horses backed up slowly; they trembled, their skin was wet with sweat.

"We are willing to let you pass," said the tom-cat, "but you must first drink a health to my sweetheart, the big Cypress-cat, Marioma, whom you see here at my side. Poets could never find words to sing of such beauty as hers. No more charming creature could ever be found, for my tom-cat eye, than the Cypress-cat, Marioma."

"Yah-pss—," warned the little kitten, jealously. But, quite undisturbed, the mighty sultan went on:

"I demand that you pay her homage by drinking from this cup."

"Never." The whip whizzed through the air. "Get-up, horses,—go!"

"Mew-mew," sang the cats, surrounding the cart in a circle. High on their hind legs reared the horses, their smooth hoofs sliding dangerously along the slippery pavement.

> "Clink with me,
> You will fare fine,
> Drink with me
> Sparkling new wine."

"Never!" cried the driver.

The cats yelled and closed their ranks, while the tom-cat laughed with scorn.

"Then you cannot go through. Driver and farmers, you will never reach the market in Delft to sell your butter and eggs. Go back."

Never get to Delft? The farmers began to mutter. It would be sad, indeed, if they could not trade their butter and eggs for money and merchandise. Always they brought home something from the city of Delft—

broadcloth and boys' caps, and cookies for the children. They did not want to be halted, but how were they to go forward?

Suddenly the driver rose up in his seat and shouted boldly:

"In God's name let us pass!"

At sound of those magic words, whoosh! the power of the phantoms vanished. The tom-cat and his comrades turned around in a flash. Pell-mell they ran back to the Locks. They pushed, they shoved, and now they never once asked who was in greatest favor with the sultan. Nay, the sultan rushed along in the crowd, with no more courage nor strength than the smallest, weakest kitten. What one of all that evil band could stand before the name of God? The one who first reached the harbor, dug with her sharp nails in the sand, where the nut-shell had been buried. Now she had it uncovered and threw it before her on the ground. The tiniest kittens accustomed to playing with ball and yarn, took hold of the shell and rolled it on till they dropped it in the water. For a moment it sank. Then, lo, it bobbed up to the surface again. It enlarged on all sides; the pin-head became a rudder, the shell, the ship; the pins turned into masts with white and stately sails. The cats jumped aboard, and during the jump they took on the forms of women, wrapped in sail-cloth; all save the fat tom-cat, who once more became a helms-man, wearing a red flannel shirt. The ship moved. The sails caught the wind. Away went that crazy crew.

It was quiet in the city of Vlaardingen as if nothing whatever had happened. The farmers drove on down the road. Never get to Delft? Indeed! There were plenty of cookies brought home for the farmer's children at night fall.

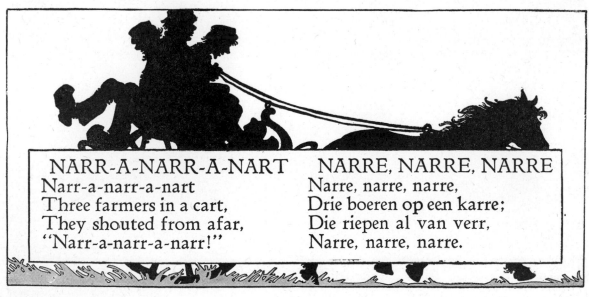

NARR-A-NARR-A-NART	NARRE, NARRE, NARRE
Narr-a-narr-a-nart	Narre, narre, narre,
Three farmers in a cart,	Drie boeren op een karre;
They shouted from afar,	Die riepen al van verr,
"Narr-a-narr-a-narr!"	Narre, narre, narre.

ZACHARIUS AND HIS SISTER
Zacharias En Zyn Zusje
Zacharius and his sister,
Saw a swan one day,—
He said, "It is a sea-gull."
She said, "It's a rooster, I say!"
Then along came Simon Willie;
He said, "Both of you are silly!"

The graceful Town Hall shown in this picture is in the lovely old town of Veere, now a dwindling Zeeland village. Many artists go to the Island of Walcheren just to paint it.

JAKIE, STAND STILL
Jaapje, Sta Still
I said one day, "Jake!" I said one day, "Jake!"
And I said one day, "Jakie, stand still!"
And why should I stand still, I pray?
I've never done anything wrong, I say!
I said one day, "Jake!" I said one day, "Jake!"
And I said one day, "Jakie, stand still!"

These children are in the costume of the villages of Spakenberg and Bunschoten in Utrecht.

65

Hans Hannekemaier in Middleburg

A Tale of the Province of Zeeland

HANS HANNEKEMAIER walked along with his scythe on his back. He had come from Germany with the other Hannekemaiers, as he did every summer, to mow the grass in Holland. For this he would get good wages and be well fed some fine day, but alack, that day was not now. In the sorry now, he had no money, he had no work, and he was hungry—dear me, but he was hungry. There he was in the island province of Zeeland, as beautiful and fair as any spot in Holland—scarlet poppies blooming in masses on the green sides of the dikes, buttercups and daisies amongst the fields of grain—but where was there food for Hans, that honest day-laborer, Hans? Now and then he met pretty girls in dainty lace caps, carrying two green pails hung from a bright blue yoke across their shoulders. They smiled, they laughed, but they gave no food to Hans.

The road was narrow, no more than eight feet wide, paved with brick and lined with poplars and willows. As Hans drew nearer to Middleburg, crowds of people passed him, men and girls on bicycles, swarms and throngs of bicycles, the girls in wide lace caps and great full skirts, that flapped like banners in the breeze. Whole families, too, went by in high-backed wagons with canvas tops, a blaze of brilliant color—wagons painted bright green with a border of gay tinted flowers, hoops that held up the canvas top, springs and shafts of sapphire blue, and wheels of vivid scarlet. It was market day in Middleburg. That was where they were going. But alas, what good was market-day to a Hannekemaier who had not a cent in his pocket?

By-and-by Hans came to Middleburg. Never had he seen elsewhere a merrier jumble of color, defying the dignified soberness of ancient brick or stone—here a blue and yellow shutter, there a shutter red and white, now one flaunting shamelessly a daring orange and black. In fact, the one and only thing Hans did not find to his liking in the ancient town of Middleburg was the fact that he had to walk in the streets. The good burghers, it seems, had reserved the sidewalks in front of their houses for their own use altogether, by fencing them in with railings of iron or shining brass.

Hans walked under a gateway of brick and stone, and there he was in Abbey Square, sunlight filtering down through the dense shade of fine old trees and playing hide and seek amongst their moss-grown trunks, quaint old buildings shutting in the place on every side, with tall gable roofs and turrets, and the soaring tower of Long John high above the rest. For many an age and century, had Long John stood like a guardian spirit protecting the town of Middleburg and speaking out with his one and forty bells eight times every hour, beautiful, grave, deliberate, a silvery music of chimes. But what Long John said to Hans, as he stood with his scythe on his shoulder, was only this, alas! "It's dinner time, dinner time, dinner time!"

And, as if that were not enough, when Long John had ceased to ring out, Crazy Betsy spoke up with her bells. And Crazy Betsy was the town-hall clock, who never would keep time with Long John, but had her own way, like a woman, and declared the hour insistently, exactly when she chose. And Crazy Betsy, in order to disagree, as usual, with Long John, cried out to Hans: "It's past dinner time, past dinner time, past dinner time, I say!"

So Hans set off for Town-Hall Square, the center of life in the city. Scarcely could he make his way through the narrow streets for the swarms of people that thronged them. There came crowds of girls, four abreast, laughing and talking and taking up all the road with their swishing balloon-like skirts and huge flapping oval caps, and, behind them, four young men in full black trousers, double-breasted vests, short coats reaching to their hips, queer little flat, round, black beaver hats, and round silver buckles, like mounds of fish eggs, clasping their belts and the bright green ties at their necks. Who was Hans, pray tell, that such belles and beaux as these should break their lines and make way for him to pass?

At last, however, Hans found himself in Town-Hall Square. The place was crowded with booths for the selling of everything under the sun, and over this, like a decorous Mrs. Grundy, stood the handsome, Gothic town-hall, its delicate turrets and finely wrought carvings in stone like the lace that adorns an old woman's gown or towers up on her head-dress, its three rows of dormer windows in the slope of its tall, tall roof like so many eyes watching out, determined to see that all should go well in the crowded square below. Indeed, the town-hall was the handsome old dame for whom Crazy Betsy was the voice.

But Hans, alack, had eyes in all that thronging place, only for the traveling waffle and poffertje restaurants that went about the country like merry-go-rounds to markets, kermises and fairs. How gay they were, with ferns, and flowers, and muslin curtains, and ribbons. And everyone was eating poffertjes and waffles—Um, how good they smelled! One could eat four and twenty poffertjes and feel he had only begun! But Hans, poor Hans, could only stand around and watch the cook as he baked them, twisting the little round pancaky things all covered with butter and sugar and pressing them into the hollows of a tray that stood over the fire. Hundreds he baked at a time, and look over there! Another cook made waffles, with eight moulds going at once. When the eighth was filled from the pail of batter at his side, the waffle in the first was done, a crisp brown oblong wafer. A woman put the waffle on a plate and spread it with butter and sugar, and then it was whisked away from under Hans's very nose to serve some other more fortunate being, leaving to poor Hans naught but the whiff of its fragrance.

Hans was so miserable that he began to cry. O dear, how miserable he felt. Then a little old granny passed by, peddling milk and pushing her cart with difficulty. When she saw poor Hans's grief, she stopped, for she felt sorry for him, and that was something which Hans had not often experienced in his life.

"Why do you cry, my good man?" she asked.

"I'm so hungry," said Hans. "For three days I haven't eaten a mouthful."

"Well, well, poor man, wait a moment! Here is some barley and a little milk. If you cook the two together, you will have a delicious porridge."

"Thank you kindly," said Hans, and away he ran in great delight to an inn which lifted its gabled front nearby on the square.

"Will you let me have a kettle to boil a little barley?" he asked of the host politely, and the host, who was in a good humor, winked at his guests and said: "All right, my man, go ahead."

Nobody was standing near the stove when Hans put his pan on the fire. He noticed, however, that there was not much barley to cook, so he folded his hands and said:

"Oh, dear Lord, I haven't much milk and barley, and so I pray you make it grow, make it rise, make it more, much more."

Soon little bubbles rose and then broke around the edge of the kettle, and a tough skin appeared across the top of the milk. Then slowly, slowly, the milk began to rise. Hans cut a merry caper.

"My prayer is answered," he cried. "The barley rises and becomes more. I shall be able to get all I want." He thought that presently he would have a whole bucket full, and his eyes began to glow with greed. He would make it more and more and more! Such power he had! He would not stop till he had enough for a week! How quickly the porridge rose!

"Now I have almost a pan full," squeaked the happy Hans, but still he was not content. "Dear Lord," he cried, "let it grow still more and more and more."

Yes, the food did grow, but too much, alas. It rose to the edge, it boiled over, it spattered on the hot stove, it burned up and vanished in smoke. Then Hans saw that he had gone too far. He had asked too much! He had been too greedy. He must stop this swelling at once. So he cried:

"Dear Lord, let it stop swelling now. It has swollen too much!"

Nothing availed. He had to look on while the precious delicacy all boiled over and was lost. And then the cook came along and scolded him soundly, as only a Dutch woman can when her housekeeping is interfered with. And she cried out:

"Don't you know enough to take milk off the fire when it boils? Don't you know it will bubble over and boil to nothing, if you don't?"

So Hans stole sadly out of the place. And he sat down by the roadside and wept again, while Crazy Betsy and Long John rang him a sad refrain.

The next morning, however, Hans went out in the country and hired himself to a farmer. In the farmer's house there was porridge on the table. Hans looked at it cross-eyed. How it steamed!

"Do I get something to eat if I'm going to work?" he said.

The farmer laughed.

"Of course, Hans! Three meals a day, breakfast, dinner and supper."

"And, if I may ask, do I get breakfast first?"

"Yes, Hans, you may begin immediately. The porridge is steaming on the table. Eat as much as you like."

So Hans fell to with a will, and shut his eyes with pleasure. O, but it was good, and after fasting so long! When he had finished, the farmer said:

"Now to work, Hans! Working comes after eating."

"Well said, boss," answered Hans, and he got up from his chair. At the door, however, he stopped.

"Boss," he said, "may I ask you something?" He looked as true-hearted as a young doggie, that never has been beaten.

"Surely, Hans," said the farmer.

"Boss! I was thinking . . . . . why should I wait till noon? **Can't** I get my dinner now?"

"Dinner—why Hans, it's too early." But the farmer's wife gave her husband a nudge and whispered in his ear:

"Let him eat his dinner now. It will save us time. If he waits until twelve o'clock, he will have to walk all the way in from the field, and we will be paying him for the time he spends in walking. Whereas, if we give him his dinner now, he can keep right on at his work without interruption at noon."

"Do you mean that?" asked the farmer surprised, and he went to Hannekemaier. "Well, that's all right," he said. "The wife will give you your dinner."

The farmer's wife had peeled her potatoes, and she put them on the fire. When they were done, she added a lump of lard as big as a fist and a couple of chunks of meat, such as Hans had never seen even in his dreams. He rubbed his eyes, as if he were living in a wonderland, but after that he made a brave attack. It went even faster than at breakfast. Although he had eaten a big plate full of Dutch porridge, it still seemed as if he were starved. As a cistern absorbs the rain after many days of drought, so his stomach absorbed the warm food. The farmer had imagined that every one could be expected to be satisfied after breakfast. But he was mistaken! Finally Hans wiped his mouth with the back of his hand, and looked at his empty plate with a sigh; then he rose with effort. Slowly he walked to the door, but many times he turned around, like a man, who says good-bye to his country.

"Now you must have had enough to eat, Hans!" laughed the farmer. "Or would you like to have some more?"

Then Hannekemaier said honestly:

"Boss, haven't I heard you say something about supper?"

"Yes, I have talked about that, but here we eat supper at night."

Nevertheless, the farmer's wife gave him another nudge, took him off in a corner and said:

"Let him have his supper too! It will save us his time, I say."

So she began immediately to cut his bread and to spread it, not stingy by any means, with fragrant, fresh yellow butter! Hans looked at this operation with the attention of a child, who is going to get something good from his godmother. She cut for him slices of "pumpernickel," not such thin ones as are eaten in the city and can be blown away by a zephyr, no, indeed, but thick ones, thick enough to scare a dainty, young lady. But Hans did not whimper. His whole face said: "Fine."

The moment that the woman cut a chunk of golden yellow cheese, which was so rich that the grease dripped from the blade, the poor fellow's eyes filled with tears, as if he were too happy for words. Yes, if he had seen his wife and children, it could not have been a happier moment for Hans than this. He leaned his head forward to smell the coming delicacy. He could eat his supper, too. No one had reason to doubt that. He took his place at the table like a prince.

"Just give me some of those sandwiches," he said.

He ate his cheeks full, without taking much time to chew. Like the burghers of Leyden after the siege, he ate, and the mountain of bread, butter and cheese disappeared before his eyes. The farmer was waiting on the door step.

"Are you almost ready, Hans?" he asked patiently.

"I'm coming, I'm coming! Here I am."

As soon as they came outdoors, Hans looked around, and breathed the cool morning air.

"You must feel like working," said the farmer, "after having eaten so heartily!"

"Working . . . . . ?" asked Hans in surprise, "to work, boss? Do you want me to work?"

"Of course! The day has hardly begun?"

"But I have had my supper! And at home we go to sleep after we have had our supper. Boss! show me the hay mow!"

The farmer could talk all he wished—at the first hay mow they passed, Hans dropped down and soon he was sleeping so soundly, that he outdid the song of the lark. The farmer tried to rouse him with fist and boot, but when Hans Hannekemaier had eaten his supper, he was accustomed to sleep, and to sleep the sleep of the just, unworried by the cares and troubles of life.

Hans Hannekemaier in Hindeloopen

HANS HANNEKEMAIER was on his way to Amsterdam where he meant to take the boat for Hindeloopen in Friesland. There he would work for his old boss. He was very tired. He had walked a long way. He panted—the scythe weighed heavily on his back. His head buzzed for sleep. He asked a passer-by:

"How far is it to Amsterdam?"

"Three hours if you walk fast."

"Three hours!" moaned Hans, and he sat by the side of the road.

But whom should he see coming along in the distance? Heinrich Hannekemaier! Hans jumped in the air for joy.

"Are you also going to Amsterdam and Hindeloopen, brother?"

"Yes," said Heinrich, "but I am so tired, brother."

"Never mind," said Hans. "I have just asked how far it is. Three hours for me alone, but if we go together, then we shall just divide the time in two. It will be only an hour and a half for each of us. Forward, brother!"

And so they came to Amsterdam, and Hans was walking along the Y, that wide arm like a bay through which the Amstel river flows into the Zuyder Zee. The boat which he meant to take for Hindeloopen rang its bell for the first time.

Hans wanted to take some money from his purse to pay his fare, and, as usual, he unwrapped his bundle, when a dime that wanted to see a little of the world also, jumped before the other money out of the bundle, slipped through Hans's thumb and first finger, somersaulted through the air, rolled over the street, turned somewhere, and Hans saw it no more. To Hans Hannekemaier it seemed, as if the world had come to an end.

"Ah, little dime," he cried, "dime, dime, where have you disappeared to? Dime, dime, I cannot find you."

The bell on the boat rang for the second time.

Hans kept on hunting, perspiration running down his forehead; the loss of a dime caused him more grief than the good-bye to his mother and father. Yes, he would far rather have lost a friend than a dime.

"Dime, dime, tell me quickly, where you have gone to. Let me hear your little voice, whisper to me where you are hiding. Ah, little dime."

But the dime stayed in his hiding place and the bell on the boat rang for the third time.

Hans found a seat on the deck, held his head with both hands, and groaned while the tears ran down his cheeks. He threw his scythe down somewhere and paid no further heed to it. Nothing pleased him now. When he reached Hindeloopen, he felt like a lover who has lost his sweetheart, and has no chance to win her back. He wanted to tell everyone about the treasure he had lost. He blamed himself a thousand times for not having been more careful. He let his head hang mournfully and kept his eyes cast down.

Did he care that here in the charming streets of this pleasant fishing village were displayed all the beautiful painted furniture, cradles, chairs, cupboards, sleds which are made in Hindeloopen? Did he look through the doorways into beautiful interiors, all lined with blue and white tiles, displaying exquisite painted woodwork and cabinets of wonderful carving groaning with curios—Delft plates, shining copper and brass, and beaten silver vessels? Did he care that the cabinet maker and his wife had brought out in front of their house a splendid cradle, just completed, all wonderfully carved and painted with stories out of the Bible? No, not he. Hans Hannekemaier saw nothing. He cared for nothing but his dime.

"Little dime, little dime, have I lost you forever?" he cried.

Suddenly he jumped, as if a crab had pinched his toes. Then he stooped down quickly. For joy he looked cross-eyed! There in the street of Hindeloopen he picked up a dime, which a fisher boy had lost. Trembling with emotion he began to talk:

"Little dime, little dime, my dear little dime, have I got you? Oh, dime, my good little dime, I could not lose you. Oh, my wonderful little dime, my sweet little dime, my darling little dime, I should not have felt so badly, I could have expected it, my own little dime. You have rolled after me all the way over the sea from Amsterdam to Hindeloopen! My faithful little dime! I thank you, little dime!"

AMSTERDAM, THAT GREAT BIG TOWN

Amsterdam, that great, big town,
Is built on piles they say;
And if that town should tumble down,
Who'd pay for it, I pray?

AMSTERDAM, DIE GROOTE STAD

Amsterdam die groote stad
Die is gebouwd op palen.
Als die stad eens ommeviel
Wie zou dat dan betalen?

The houses in Amsterdam are built up out of the water on piles. The royal palace stands on 13,659 piles.

75

MOTHER MAY I GO OUT?
Moeder Mag Ik Meegaan
Mother may I go out?
    Johnny Lyon
    He is cryin',—
    Hear him shout!
No, boy, here at home you stay,
You must keep the thieves away!

BLACK WILHELMINE
Zwart Willemyntje
Black Wilhelmine
Sat back of the screen.
What did she there?
She combed her hair.
She washed her hands
And dried them with care.

In many of the little Dutch villages such as the old fishing village of Arnemuiden in Zeeland, the houses are built so close to the street that screens of transparent dark colors are put in the windows so that passers cannot look in, though the family inside can see out.

The Wise Men of Kampen

IN HOLLAND all the wise men come from Kampen. It was in Kampen that the aldermen and the burgomaster sat close around the chimney in the town hall and deliberated long on what course to pursue when it was discovered that the burgomaster's breeches had caught fire. It was in Kampen that the aldermen decided by solemn decree to move the fireplace further back, in order to prevent such a calamity from occurring again in the future. So it is easily to be seen that Kampen was full of wise men.

Now it chanced not long ago that an Amsterdammer condescended to take a walk about his city in company with a man from Kampen.

"See," said he of Amsterdam. "How clever and fine and rich are we in this beautiful city. Look at our fine ladies and gentlemen, our splendid coaches, our canals and shipping, our stately houses all built up solidly out of the water on piles. Think of our royal palace, requiring for its foundation 13,659 piles. Look at our jewelry shops and silver shops with ships and sleighs and windmills splendidly carved out of silver. In comparison with all this, what are you fellows of Kampen? Nothing, nothing whatever. By your proverbial stupidity, you Kampeners are only our slaves. Here recognize your inferiority, man of Overysel. What you do is stupid, what we do is sensible."

The Kampener shuddered.

"Everything?"

"Everything."

"Without exception?"

"Without exception."

On hearing this sad pronouncement, the Kampener sat down right where he was on the tracks of the street railway to weep out his sorrow. There the Amsterdammer knew that his friend's life was in danger, so he pulled him up and brushed his trousers, as a father would do to a helpless little child. Then the two hobbled on their way.

At last they came to the Second Jan Steen Street, and there the Kampener saw something very strange. He stopped and opened his mouth in surprise. Then he touched the Amsterdammer's shoulder, and cried with joy: "Amsterdammer, Amsterdammer, not all Amsterdammers are sensible."

"All without distinction."

"Men and women?"

"Men and women. An Amsterdam babe-in-arms has more sense than a Kampen alderman."

"Wait a moment. Notice how yonder maid here in Amsterdam is doing her work. Look, she mops the steps, and she does not begin with the top one, but with the very lowest! Every time she moves up, she puts her dirty feet on the wood she has just finished cleaning. So her work is in vain! Do you still wish to maintain, Amsterdammer, that all Amsterdammers are sensible?"

The other disdainfully waved his hands.

"Ask her where she was born."

The Kampener hastened in her direction.

"Tell me, girlie," he asked candidly, "where do you come from?"

The maid turned around and looked in perplexity at the man.

"From Kampen, Sir, of course!" And she turned back to her work.

Such was the city of Kampen.

Now it chanced that there was once a little boy named Pietro who lived in Savoy. His parents had died, and the only possession they had left him was a little guinea pig. With this, Pietro set out into the world.

But alas! few people wanted to pay him half a penny for the privilege of seeing his guinea pig. Often the little man sat by the road side, as thin as a young birch tree, for what did he get to eat but hard, dry crusts of bread?

But still he kept on going north, to the distant country where his father had been a chimney sweep. There, he had heard, is a land of white palaces and women who wear golden caps; the fattest chickens flutter over the roads, and gentlemen with fat stomachs ride in ebony coaches. The name of this country is Holland.

So Pietro arrived in Holland and he leaped for joy. Immediately he got milk to drink which tasted like almonds, and a slice of bread with butter and cheese. Such a country, Holland! Pietro received a lot of good advice, and he wandered from city to city, to show his little guinea pig. The children especially liked to see it and pushed and shoved around the little Savoyard.

Finally Pietro came to Kampen. Ah, if he only had stayed far away! What should a person do in Kampen, if he has no business there . . . . ?

In Kampen lived a chimney sweep, who went at once to the boy, and asked him in his own language:

"Do you want to stay with me?"

"Yes!" said Pietro, and so he, the Savoyard, became a Kampen chimney sweep. He was given a clean white linen blouse, carefully starched and ironed, but in half an hour it was soiled, and he looked like a little Satan. In the beginning he got more blows than food, for Pietro did not want to go into the chimneys. He did not like to climb through the narrow holes and the soot. Nothing availed . . . . . He had sold himself to the master! So he learned to crawl through a narrow chimney, and, blacker than Sinterklaas's darkey, to greet the bright blue sky.

Often the chimney sweep and his wife talked about him.

The chimney sweep said: "Pietro stays so thin, as if he ate only blackberries and wild raspberries and bilberries in the forest. Is the boy never going to be a real man of our guild? Look at those hands, not much fatter than those of a little salamander. Be sure to give him bread spread with an inch of butter; give him quarts of milk to drink and raw eggs from our garden; fry his bacon in lard, cut him fat ham, and pour good gravy over his peas."

Often the good man and his wife complained to each other when they saw their apprentice continue to look like a skeleton. Yes, when the boss stood below in the room while the boy was climbing up the chimney, he worried:

"There that blade of grass blows up again, more by the draft than by his own efforts. How shall I ever teach that boy to eat enough?"

Under these circumstances Pietro continued to look like a straw, and everyone in Kampen despaired of his future. Such a bag of bones!

But, to his honor it must be said, that as a chimney sweep, he was one among thousands. No speck of soot was left where his broom had scrubbed, and in course of time he succeeded his master as chimney sweep to Kampen.

By-and-by he fell in love with a neighbor girl, named Truitje. But young love does not make one fat either. As soon as Truitje noticed that Pietro stood still when she passed, and opened his mouth on account of her wondrous beauty, she looked the other way; and with that began the usual game of love. Of course, Truitje had a girl friend, named Aaltje. When these two thought that Pietro was waiting to see them, they let him wait for half an hour.

Then they walked arm in arm in the street, and started to giggle immediately. They pinched each other's arms, wiggled themselves and passed him screaming with laughter.....but, don't worry, mothers of sons! The third time that they treated him so cruelly, Truitje looked back one moment. Then she told her other girl friends how foolishly Pietro acted, and she laughed all to herself.

"He thinks perhaps, that I shall take him! I won't!" she said and believed it; but when she was alone in her room, late at night, she looked at the moon and the quiet light which it wove over land and sky. She listened to the whispering of the leaves and was troubled.

Still she made fun of poor Pietro. When she sat together with her girl friends, her tongue told a thousand instances of his awkwardness and his boorishness, and the patience with which he insisted. She would not think of taking him, such a run-away chimney sweep, such a guinea pig beggar, such a bare-footer, such a penniless purse; but while saying this, she felt miserable. And Pietro? He stood in Long Street, like a sign in front of a tobacco shop, the smoking darky. He took Truitje's laughing seriously and thought that he had lost out. Then some people grew certain that he would dwindle down into a real skeleton.

But one day Truitje passed him, holding a bunch of flowers, which she had picked on Kampen Island; and, by accident, she dropped two or three daisies to the ground. These Pietro picked up in spite of his sooty, black hands!

The next Sunday, after he had washed himself nice and clean, he went to church; later he waited for her outside. Who could believe that Pietro and Truitje walked together? And why did she ask him to go home with her? How did it happen that Truitje's mother had bought a tart? Poor Pietro. Now he was like the fish in a net, and there was no use to struggle. He was accepted by Truitje before he realized it. He saw himself walking arm in arm with the pretty young girl without understanding "how" it had all come about.

At the wedding feast, Truitje already showed her wifely sense of duty. The best bites were for the bridegroom. Shame on him! Did he eat only one plate of chicken soup? She called the waiter and he brought in a second.

"Pietro!" she begged, "now eat it all!"

She picked out the biggest piece of pike for him, and from the roasted meat, she put the pieces with lots of fat on his plate. She whispered so that he alone could hear it:

"When you marry me, I must look out for you. You understand very well, that you cannot longer be the grasshopper you are!"

Poor Pietro! Modest little Truitje had learned to cook from her mother, and she knew how to make all kinds of things out of flour, sugar, butter, eggs and citron peel, out of calf's head, vinegar and spices. Gradually, slowly but surely, she fattened Pietro, as though he had been a goose or a pullet.

"You would never know him," she said with pride to her friends. Then one day Pietro noticed that it was harder for him to climb up in the chimneys than it had been before. It seemed that his limbs sat tight in their hinges. Groaning, he started and moaning, he finished his work.

At last there came a spring after a very long winter, during which Pietro's stomach, thanks to Truitje's sausages and the pig's heels and ears in the thick pea soup, had taken on such enormous dimensions as had never before been seen in Kampen. He went out and came to the wife of the town-clerk, who immediately took him to the chimney. The lady was in a hurry.

"Come, Pietro!" she said. Then beads of perspiration appeared on his forehead, and he wriggled his neck into the narrow opening. His arms went up, his shoulders followed with more difficulty. His back and chest, too, found room. But his fat moved down only till it struck the layers of his stomach, where it formed new lumps. The moment came when he could not go any farther. He was caught in the chimney. He tried to jump down. He could not. His legs were sprawling out of the chimney, to the great dismay of the housewife, who finally came to a brave decision and seized him by his feet. This act of charity was ill repaid. For Pietro kicked her so that she fell backward. The maid, who heard the noise and came running into the room, saw only a pair of black, swinging legs and she exclaimed:

"It's the devil, madam, the devil himself!"

The neighbors came to their rescue, and they, too, thought that Satan was acting up. But the lady assured them: it was not the devil, but good, fat Pietro, who had been treated by his wife like a Christmas rabbit, and who had to undergo nearly the same punishment. From different sides, they now approached him. They counted, one, two, three; and at the third count they pulled with all their might. Hard work! Inch by inch, the Savoyard came down, until he finally stood in the room, decorated with soot. When he was set free, they gave a loud hurrah! But with all that, the town-clerk's wife did not have her chimney swept! And there was no other chimney sweep but Pietro in all the city of Kampen......

It was not only to this gentlewoman either that Pietro's excessive fatness caused trouble. Rich and poor, without exception, suffered. Poor Truitje got it, you may believe! And she had done her best, the good soul. Now the wrath of the whole city was upon her; and immediately, as soon as her husband's livelihood was in danger, she began to feed him less. What did he get from then on? Potatoes with thin gravy, or watery cabbage, or tough, boiled beef. No more rich sauces, no creamy tarts!

In Kampen people were anxiously waiting for the shrinking of his stomach. Until that time the chimneys were unswept. Their patience was put on trial. There was no other subject of conversation, either for the carpenter's Jennie, or the burgomaster's wife.

But Pietro's stomach, instead of diminishing, was swelling more and more. It filled up the cavities, which before had existed in some places. Now it was impossible for him to look over the hill which was formed at his waist line. He wobbled with little steps, like a child learning to walk.

"Woe, woe to us!" cried the house mothers, and their voices were heard in the town-council meeting. "What is to become of us? One of these days with our chimneys so dirty, all of Kampen is going to catch fire, and our fine new Jan van der Heyden fire engine will do us no good whatever!"

About less serious things council meetings have been held in our country. All the members of the council, old and young alike, were present. They talked busily. Indeed, it was quite a case: on the one hand a stout chimney sweep, on the other a narrow chimney. They did neither fit nor match. But were those, here gathered, not the wise men of Kampen who always knew what to do?

The second oldest council member—his name is lost, although his wisdom is still possessed by his descendants—rose, coughed, wiped his spectacles and his nose, blinked his eyes a number of times and said:

"The man, who stays fat, will get stuck in the chimneys; he cannot get in, nor out. Pietro looks more like a barrel than a man, and he won't get thin. What remains to be done by us? Only one thing, my friends! Let us widen the chimneys. Let us decree that the Kampen chimneys have more stomach than they have had so far. Then Pietro can keep on sweeping as of old!"

To this the aldermen agreed. It was, they said, the only way. So the Kampeners tore down their chimneys and built them all over, wide and fat. They became chimneys, which looked like a chimney sweep. Pietro joyfully climbed up and his broom swept the soot.

"Now he can get still stouter!" the people said. "It won't hurt our chimneys!"

LADY, WILL YOU FORBID YOUR LITTLE BOY?
Juffrouw Will Je Je Jongetje Verbieden
Lady, will you forbid your little boy
Evenings to come to my door?—
Ting-a-ling-a-ling! Lift the latch!
"Lady, will you buy a match?"

This picture was suggested by a row of houses painted by the Dutch artist, Vermeer (1632-1675).

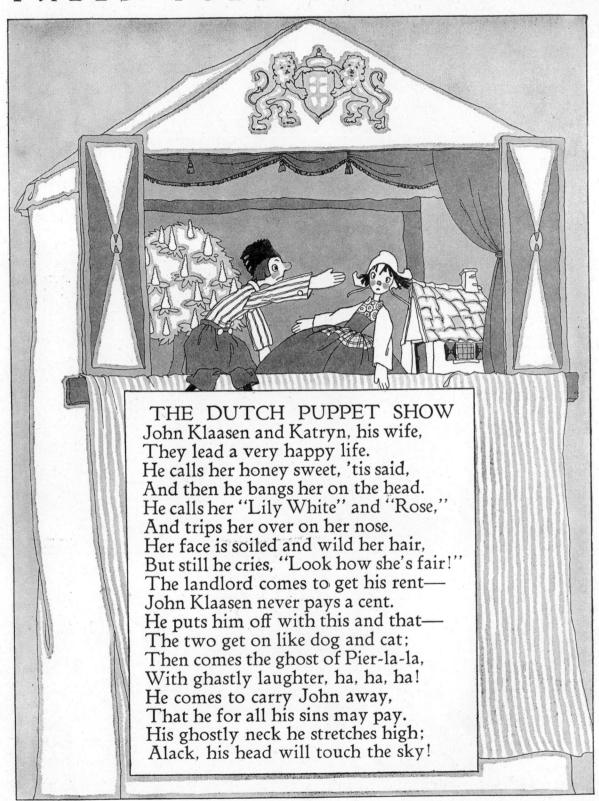

THE DUTCH PUPPET SHOW

John Klaasen and Katryn, his wife,
They lead a very happy life.
He calls her honey sweet, 'tis said,
And then he bangs her on the head.
He calls her "Lily White" and "Rose,"
And trips her over on her nose.
Her face is soiled and wild her hair,
But still he cries, "Look how she's fair!"
The landlord comes to get his rent—
John Klaasen never pays a cent.
He puts him off with this and that—
The two get on like dog and cat;
Then comes the ghost of Pier-la-la,
With ghastly laughter, ha, ha, ha!
He comes to carry John away,
That he for all his sins may pay.
His ghostly neck he stretches high;
Alack, his head will touch the sky!

The shivers go down Johnny's back,
Alack for such a sight, alack!
But Johnny's wise as any fox;
He cries: "Come jump into this box.
And ere you carry me away,
I beg that you will show me, pray,
If you can shrink that neck down low,
As well as stretch it high, you know."
A proud old ghost is Pier-la-la,
He'll prove what he can do, ha, ha!
He jumps into the box to show
His awful neck can shrink down low.
Then Johnny bangs the cover to,
And locks it without more ado.
He hears the landlord coming in,
And leaves the boxed-up ghost to him.
Away, runs John, and ah, ah, ah,
In Landlord's face pops Pier-la-la.

The St. Nicholas Legend

Look, yonder comes the schooner,
  All the way from Spain.
There stands good St. Nicholas,
  Coming back again.
Frisking up and down the deck,
  See his horsie go!
How prettily the pennants
  Flutter to and fro!
His servant smiles upon us—
  With gifts his bags are rich—
Who's good, shall have some goodies.
  Who's naughty, gets a switch!

Every winter the good old bishop, St. Nicholas, comes in his ship over the sea from Spain. And who is that with him? It is his servant, a little Moor, named Black Pete. They are bringing goodies and toys for the children of Holland.

Ages and ages ago, a certain man became so poor that he saw no way out of his difficulty save to sell his three beautiful daughters. But one night some one came secretly and dropped a large sum of money through a broken window pane into the poor man's house. The next night, a second gift of gold suddenly fell down the chimney. On the third night the poor man, grateful beyond all words, waited to find out who it was that was thus relieving his dire distress. When he heard a noise at the door, he suddenly flung it open and fell at the feet of the man outside. Then he saw it was St. Nicholas and he cried: "O Nicholas, servant of the Lord, wherefore didst thou hide thy good deeds?" And from that time forth, everyone has known that it is St. Nicholas who brings presents during the night. St. Nicholas brings gifts to every child in Holland

except those who have been naughty. The naughty ones, alack, get nothing but a switch.

A few weeks before St. Nicholas Day, all the shops and candy stores are gay and everyone is happy. Throughout November and even before, St. Nicholas sees and hears everything that goes on. Aye, he knows exactly what children do not deserve presents. At night he rides over the roofs on his white horse and sometimes he listens at the chimneys. Then many a little child puts before the fire a wooden shoe filled with hay and a piece of rye bread for St. Nicholas's horse. In the morning it often happens that the hay and bread are gone. The good white steed has eaten them, and in their place are left candy and little spice cakes for the child.

It is on St. Nicholas Eve, the fifth of December, that the good saint rides. In his magic red mantle he can go all over Holland in a single night, and the children sing:

> *Sinterklaas, good holy man,*
> *Put your best red tabard on;*
> *Ride in it to Amsterdam,*
> *From Amsterdam to Spain!*
> *   Apples come from Orange*
> *   Pears from off the trees,*
> *Sinterklaas, come please.*

But if you want Sinterklaas to come, you must be good. And if ever you see a little black boy, be careful how you treat him. He might be Sinterklaas's darky.

Once a Moor walked the streets as black as pitch. The sun shone on his curly head, so he put up his parasol. This, little Ferdinand saw, as he ran with a flag in his hand. Casper, too, with a piece of cake, and Billy, rolling his hoop, gladly joined the party. These three made fun of the Moor and laughed at his black skin. Then came good Sinterklaas with an ink well, a huge one. He said, "Come, boys, listen here. Leave that little Moor alone. It is not his fault that he is not white like you." The boys, however, paid no heed. They continued to laugh at the poor little Moor. This Sinterklaas did not like. He took firm hold of the boys. Little men, now look out. He put them with his strong hand, Caspar, Bill and Ferdinand, in the ink well, black and deep. Crying was of no use. When they ran away, they were black, all three, as black as the little Moor.

On St. Nicholas Eve, the housewives spread out a large white sheet in the center of the floor, and round it stand the children with sparkling eyes and flushed faces eagerly waiting for Sinterklaas. As soon as the clock says it is nearly time for him to appear, they all begin to sing:

Good St. Nick'las, bonny, bonny, bonny,
Give a gift to little Johnny,
Fill my little wooden shoe—
Good St. Nick'las, I thank you.

Sometimes the first inkling the children get of the saint's arrival is a rattling of chains outside. His little Moor has done that. How mysterious! How creepy! Then a shower of sweets bursts into the room, and St. Nicholas appears in his long robe and his tall hat and his bishop's crook. With great dignity, he enters and calls the children by name. To each he points out his faults or praises him. The children are deeply impressed. How strange that Sinterklaas always knows if they have been good or bad. He tells them all to be obedient and helpful to their parents. Then he hands out the presents from a great basket which he has brought. In the rear stands Black Pete with an open sack in one hand. In that he will put all the naughty boys and girls, and he holds a rod, too, which he shakes with vigor. You'd better be good and look out for Black Pete's switch!

Once a surly old abbot scolded that he would not permit St. Nicholas songs to be sung in his church. They were childish, worldly, foolish, he said. But he was dragged out of bed in the dead of night and switched like a naughty boy with Sinterklaas's rod, till he changed his surly old mind and opened up his heart to the joy of St. Nicholas Day. Let everyone, who is not good, beware of a Black Pete's rod.

Before leaving, St. Nicholas draws out a bagful of goodies and scatters them abroad, while the children scramble for them till they are sent off to bed. Then the sheet with the mess is cleared up and the older people begin their celebration.

Next morning the children run eagerly to the chimney where, the night before, they have set out their shoes. These are full of candy presents, the child's initials in chocolate; cookies made in the shapes of birds, beasts, and fishes; large dolls of cake; cake baked like St. Nicholas or Charlemagne on horseback; sugar candy hearts, slippers, scissors or St. Nicholas's boat.

It must never be known by old or young, who gives the gifts on St. Nicholas Day. No, they must be mysteriously handed out and done up in all sorts of queer disguises. Small things are sometimes baked into a loaf of bread, or done up a number of times into packages quite enormous. The longer it takes before the present is found, the more successful the surprise. And so the happy day goes. Everywhere are smiling faces, mirth and jollity. Good feeling makes all men brethren on this, the most beloved of merry Dutch holidays.

THE STORK
Ooievaar

Storky-lork,
Storky-stork,
Steal a twig,
Stork loves babies small and big.

LITTLE, LITTLE LADDYKIN
Klein Klein Kleutertje

Little, little laddykin, what are you doing here?
You beat your little drum and make a fearful noise to hear!
Your mother'll surely scold you; your daddy'll spank, I say!
Little, little laddykin, you'd better run away!

Little, little laddykin, why are you in the street?
You cannot keep on playing for it's very much too late!
Your mother'll surely scold you; your daddy'll spank, I say!
Little, little laddykin, you'd better run away!

This picture was suggested by a painting of the Dutch artist, Peter de Hooch (1630-1681).

The Charlemagne Saga of Sittard

A Tale from the Province of Limburg

FROM the Batavians, the Frisians, and the Belgians, bravest of all the Celts whom the Romans had found and ruled in the swamp-land, later known as Holland, the Franks had made a district of the mighty Frankish empire. In the year 800, Charlemagne was Emperor of the Franks, and he had welded into one great whole, those unrelated peoples who lived in France and Germany, Holland and Belgium, Switzerland and Hungary, yes even Italy and Spain; for one and all, they owned him their sovereign lord. And the Emperor dwelt at Aix-la-Chapelle, but often he wandered over into the nearby province of Limburg.

Night came quickly under the arched roof of the forest, much more quickly than in the open fields, where daylight lingered still. In the forest all grew dumb and dark as soon as the sun went down. But the lonely horseman did not notice this. He did not notice that his companions were no longer by his side. He had followed the deer for many hours, and still his horse carried him on. He wanted amusement, something to do, to occupy his thoughts. Rest was his enemy, for memories were gnawing his heart, the fretful sorrow of never forgotten days.

"Emma," he sighed heavily, "Emma, my sister.". . . . .

This sad recollection muffled all joy at the court of Aix-la-Chapelle, the young imperial city, and, at the sound of this name, each courtier bowed his head with understanding sorrow. Then black shadows passed by which no glitter could overcome.

"Emma," sighed the horseman.

The reins were hanging loosely over the neck of the tired horse. The long blue coat of the hunter lay folded in the saddle. Wearily and slowly, the horse found his way through the thick, tangled underbrush.

The horseman woke up from his dreams. It was dark around him. Where were his companions? How long had he roamed alone? The deer, the hunted deer, had led him astray . . .

A new shadow sank on his brow. For seven years the name of Eginhart had never been mentioned before him. The emperor had fought battle after battle, had subdued Saragossa, had seen Byzantium at his feet, and baptized Widukind, the Saxon, but Emma had not left his thoughts for a moment, and Eginhart's treason to him.

He was Charlemagne.

He had turned Emma out for ever,—and without forgiveness. That she loved Eginhart, was her crime. The Emperor's sister loved the Emperor's secretary, so far beneath her in rank. How Charles had honored and loved him, but what had been his loyalty? Had not Emma carried her lover out of her home on her back, that his tracks in the snow might not betray how he had come to visit her?

Exiles they had been from that day,—homeless wanderers in the forests of Limburg between the Rhine and the Maas.

The night grew darker. The hunter blew his horn. The sound found no answer, but died away under the heavy foliage. All the silence listened.

Then there seemed to shine a star in the night of dark leaves about him. It glimmered and went out. But it glittered again, a small red light.

"Thank God," thought the emperor, "it is a human dwelling."

Before him stood a wretched hut in the midst of a clearing. An old woman appeared in the door. The sky was still light above the open spot in the forest, though the sun had long gone down.

"Where am I?" he asked.

She looked at him without answering.

"Is Aix-la-Chapelle far from here?"

"Aix" . . . . she repeated astonished.

"What time is it then?" he asked again.

She looked up at the sky: "One hour after sunset."

Lost in thoughts, he passed his hand over his forehead, and said to himself, in the Frankish tongue, which was spoken at his court: "Si tard . . . .," that is to say, "So late!"

The woman had come nearer; she had heard the word, but did not understand, for she was a woman of Limburg, not a Frank.

"Do you have to go to Aix, Sir?" she asked humbly.

He alighted.

"You must be a gentleman of rank," she muttered. She could tell it by the leather straps around his legs, the sandals on his feet; she could tell it by the fine linen of his garment and by his sword and sheath. "Sir," she said meekly, "if you wish to take what I can offer you, it is all yours. My home is poor and there is no bed, but the one of leaves and dried moss. There is nothing but stale bread and milk . . . ."

The emperor, bowing his head under the low door post, entered and sat beside the blazing fire at the wooden table opposite the poor woman, who waited on him with respect.

He did not say much and looked in the flames, while he ate his scanty meal.

But the woman looked at him attentively.

"Sir," she said, "we who live lonely in the woods, think that all the high lords in the empire are happy. But you are not happy."

"Did you think that Emperor Charles is happy, too?" he returned.

"No," answered the woman, "he certainly is not. Sir, have you children or relatives, perhaps?"

"Yes," he answered and turned his glance away.

"Would you turn out a young girl, a sister?"

"If she sinned . . . ."

She shook her head. "You would forgive, sir, you would not hate . . . . But the emperor hates."

"And does he hate unjustly?" Charlemagne enquired.

"Hatred is always injustice. Whosoever wants to be happy, forgives others, and tries to do better himself."

Charles rose, provoked. Then he bent his head and looked in the fire. For a while no one spoke.

"Do you know about Emma, the emperor's sister?" he then asked, more mildly.

"I have seen her once," said the woman, slowly and sadly. "Now she lives with Eginhart between here and Aix in the forest. They lack less than others, for they are happy in each other. But if you, my lord, should see the emperor in his magnificence, pray tell him from a poor woman in the lonely forest, that one thing mars his glory."

"And what is that?" mumbled Charlemagne.

"That he has refused to forgive."

That evening Charles did not speak one word more.

All night long he sat musing near the fire. At sunrise he arose. The morning light fell clearly on his face. His eyes rested on the old woman before him. "Thank you," he said, showing his emotion, "for what you did to a stranger and for what you taught the emperor."

The old woman was startled. "The emperor," she exclaimed, and stared in his beaming countenance.

"Today," he went on, "nothing shall mar his glory."

So he mounted his horse and rode away.

When the distant dwellers in the forest came to the woman in her lonely hut, they found her sitting with bowed head. They wanted to know what had happened, but she would not tell them. "Now the emperor's greatness shall lack nothing," was all she said. In spite of her words, however, she did not know what had changed him. Nay, she was far too humble and innocent of conceit, to think that such an old woman as she, had softened an emperor's heart. But she remembered a word, over which she was puzzling—a word he had spoken, which she had not understood. Perhaps it was a magic word which had loosened his tight-drawn heart-strings and let in the light of forgiveness. "Si

tard," he had said. "Si tard." And until the wise man should come who could explain it, she insisted that that was the word which had wrought the magic change; and the good folk held the word in such high esteem that they called their village by it, Sittard. Yea, Sittard it is to this day.

But what the emperor in his magnificence had learned "so late," became the joy of his old age. When he summoned Emma to him and she threw herself in his arms, the clocks of the imperial city announced the summit of his glory.

97

The Basilisk of Utrecht

A Tale from the Province of Utrecht

YOU must know that the province of Utrecht is quite different from other provinces; for it was in Utrecht in the year 659, that the first apostle to the Netherlands, Willebrord of Northumbria, appeared to preach the word of Christ. And it was from Utrecht that the light of Christianity spread abroad through the dusky groves of Woden and the darkness of heathenesse. And so, when the different districts of the Low-Lands, created by the Emperor Charlemagne, grew slowly into the great Duchy of Brabant, with a duke to reign over it, and the counties of Holland, Flanders, Gelderland and Friesland, with counts to reign over them, look what happened to Utrecht. Utrecht became a bishopric with a bishop at its head. And for many generations, the Bishop of Utrecht was the head of the church in those lands.

So, of course, it is to be expected that the people of Utrecht knew far more than others concerning the art of being good. It is also to be expected that these same good folk of Utrecht must be particularly on their guard to keep out what was evil.

"Yes," said they, "we must watch out that no evil enters here!" And did they mean, perchance, to watch their own hearts, as Willebrord had taught them, "Blessed are the pure in heart!" No, not they! They gathered together and debated the question. They hemmed and hawed and argued. And then they said:

"What we must guard against in our land is a basilisk. The Evil One would like nothing better than to send into our midst a basilisk."

Now a basilisk was a creature which had a body covered with bristling spines and the head of a lizard whence flashed hideous eyes of fire,— all the grannies of Utrecht were very sure about that! And if one but looked straight into the monster's flaming eyes, zip, sizz, bang! that one would be consumed to naught but a heap of ashes,—so the worthy grannies had told every child in Utrecht.

Well, while the wise-men held forth in meeting, concerning the possibility of the coming of a basilisk, a young man among them stood up, and flatly pooh-poohed the whole matter.

"What is all this talk of a creature with spines and eyes of fire?" he said. "Look you, burning hatred in our own souls is the only basilisk against which we need to keep guard, the only basilisk whose flame could consume us to ashes!"

But the older people frowned darkly upon such nonsense as this Who was he, pray tell, to speak up like that in a gathering of his elders?

Didn't he know that a basilisk had appeared in Friesland in the year 513, and more to the same effect? Besides, it was easier to watch out against a creature with spines and eyes of fire than to be forever watching one's heart and trying to keep that pure. So they pounded the floor with their canes and wagged their heads wisely and said:

"The best way to guard against the coming of a basilisk is to keep an eye on the roosters."

And that was well-reasoned wisdom. What wise-man would not agree? If you wish to guard against evil, just keep an eye on the roosters! The old men and the old women, the young men and the young women, the very boys and girls, from that moment on, kept faithful watch of the roosters. In spite of their vigilance, however, a certain rooster escaped them. Off he ran to Rag-pickers' Hill, and there he laid an egg,— that sly old rooster, he laid an egg on the rubbish heap. Of course, nobody actually saw the rooster lay the egg, but from what came later to pass, the grannies all agreed that a rooster must have laid it. Then along came a mud-turtle and sat on the egg and kept it warm, until one day it burst open. Well, what would you have? Out of that egg crawled a basilisk! And there was the very evil that the good folk of Utrecht had long been expecting! Ah, ah! I told you so! I knew it would surely happen!

Ugh! That spiny body, that lizard head! Those eyes of fire! The beast was so ugly that all creatures on earth fled from him. Nay, strange as it may seem, the basilisk fled from himself. So ugly was he, that he did not wish to see his own eyes lest he consume himself to ashes. He dreaded the sunlight which spreads out mirrors without a wrinkle on every canal and river. The darkest hole he could find,—that was the place for him. So he crawled off into the cellar of a brewery, and what better place could a basilisk find for his den than the cellar of a brewery?

By-and-by, a man went downstairs to pour the beer from a cask, but back he came in a hurry, stumbling over his feet. He had seen the light of the creature's eyes reflected red on the walls and heard the noise of his writhings! He had scarcely voice enough left to tell what he had seen. Suppose he had gazed straight into his eyes and been consumed to ashes!

O me and O my! . . . . .

How many men went down into the cellar, intending to make an end of the monster cannot now be told. It all happened too long ago. But, however many there were, not one was brave enough to finish the basilisk. A mere glimpse of the lurid glow on the dark walls of the cellar was enough to send the would-be savior scampering back to daylight. An army of men went no further than that,—down and up again!

How to free the city of Utrecht from the power of that terrible creature! Some said this. Some said that! And the city enjoyed great misery, delighting itself with groanings.

Then there came along a boy with shining face, innocent and gay, like those who are pure of heart. And he said: "I will fight the tyrant!"

Men looked on him with pity. "He will be consumed," they said.

But he came merrily and had his eyes blindfolded. Thus he would not see the flaming eyes of the basilisk. Men asked him where his weapon was. Was it a spear or a bow or a slingshot, like that the boy David used when he killed the giant, Goliath? The lad pointed to his breast where he carried a board and nothing else whatever.

"Don't you know," the onlookers asked, "that the basilisk has spines? He is a big lizard, and you will not be able to see him approach if you go down blindfolded like that!"

But the champion only smiled. He was a carefree boy, who knew neither hate nor cruelty. He would meet this danger blindfolded but with the breastplate of purity. His elders hesitated. Should they let him go down to that terrible monster? Again he smiled, and with light, youthful step he went.

The basilisk heard his footsteps, and lifted his head. His eyes were flames, but the youth did not see. He walked boldly on and felt around. Still fiercer flamed the eyes of the dragon. The boy began to laugh, confident and secure.

Slowly the lizard came nearer. If his foe was not consumed by fire, he should perish by the spines. Was there a human being who could escape the basilisk?

Then the youth took the board, which hung on his breast, and turned the other side toward the lurid darkness before him.

The basilisk sprang forward, but suddenly, what did he see? He saw his own killing eyes; for it was a mirror which the youth had carried along, a mirror, clear and clean, reflecting all things truly. And when the monster saw himself squarely, saw how ugly, how frightful he was, his own flame struck inward. Yea, his own flame consumed him till nothing at all was left, not even a heap of ashes.

Thus the city of Utrecht was delivered from the basilisk. And the boy who had delivered it, thanked God and watched out to keep his heart as clean as the spotless mirror. But the elders of Utrecht were wise men. They still continued to keep an eye on the roosters.

The Story of Lady Jacqueline

IN DAYS long past, a little girl of sixteen found herself Countess of Holland, Zeeland, Hainault, and Friesland. And being the Countess of these fair lands was almost like being a queen, in the year 1417; for a long line of brave and chivalrous counts, Dirks and Florises, Johns and Williams, had made the low-lying marsh-land fertile by building dikes to keep out the sea. They had encouraged the trade of the burghers, helped the growing towns, and raised Holland to be the companion of Kings. It might be true that Holland was still in name a part of the German Empire, owing allegiance to the Emperor, but in fact she was free, beneath the rule of her counts. She made her own laws, administered justice, named her own officers, coined her own money, and made peace or war altogether as she chose.

When the Lady Jacqueline fell heir to the Netherlands on the death of her father, Count William VI, she was staying for the time, in the ancient province of Hainault. Here there were loud "Hurrahs!" and shouts of "Long live the Lady Jacqueline," and the handsome little miss, high-spirited and charming, was hailed with joy as Lady of the Land. But it was not so in Holland, where men had always said: "We will not be ruled by a woman." In Holland were sullen murmurings and open opposition. And more than one man began to lay schemes to rob the child of her rights.

Now there were in those days in Holland, two political parties, the Codfish and the Hooks. In former times, the burghers, who stood with the counts against the power of the nobles, had called themselves Kabel-jauws or Codfish, because, they said, with a threatening glance toward their foes, "the codfish devours all the smaller fish!" Then the nobles, sharp and steel-pointed, in gleaming armor and weapons, answered: "Very well! Let the fat burghers call themselves codfish, if they like. We will be the hooks, who catch and devour the cods." And up to the day when Jacqueline came into power, those two parties had continued, the Hooks and the Cods, though they were no longer distinguished as either burgher or noble, since burghers and nobles belonged to both.

In stately procession, on handsome steeds, with a train of faithful followers, little Jacqueline and her mother came riding into Holland. Then the Hooks declared themselves for Count William's pretty daughter and accepted her as Lady of the Land, but the Cods cried noisily: "Nay, we will not have a woman! We will have as count none but John of Bavaria, the brother of William VI." And John of Bavaria, Jacqueline's uncle, was John-without-Mercy, hard of head, hard of heart, a rogue who had set himself to seize young Jacqueline's birthright because she was a girl.

Hard times began for Jacqueline. She was so young. She was little more than a child. And how great and formidable was the power arrayed against her! Nevertheless, she put herself at the head of an army and attacked the stronghold of Gorcum. She even took the city. Mere slip of a girl though she was, she led an army of men against those grim old walls and saw the line of her mail-clad foes bow their heads before her. But the deed accomplished little. Her enemies had the power of bobbing up again whenever she put them down, as though they had been a throng of corks afloat on a summer sea. Then her mother began to think: "I would do well to get the girl a husband," and she made no delay of her plan, but married Jacqueline off, with bells and flowers and ceremony, to her cousin, Duke John of Brabant, a boy of fifteen, whereby she thought to unite the provinces of Holland, Zeeland, Hainault and Friesland with Brabant. And little was Lady Jacqueline consulted in the matter. It never entered her mother's head to ask her, would she or no? Almost before she knew what plans were going forward, Jacqueline found herself sold like a bale of silk to Duke John, and away she was sent to live at her husband's court in Brabant.

Now this was the second time in her life that Jacqueline had been married off, willy-nilly, by one of her august parents. For when she was the merest slip of a child, still playing with her dolls, her father, Count William VI, to further his own political schemes, had taken her from her toys and married her to the tiny Dauphin of France, who had but recently died. And who had thought in these weddings, whether Jacqueline would be happy? All they had thought of in passing her over, was what could be gained by the deal.

But not much was gained this time, and no doubt whatever about it. The little bride found her husband, John of Brabant, a weak-minded, weak-kneed youth, loving no one but himself. He was, indeed, a simpleton, as slow of wit as though he had come from the famous town of Kampen. What would such a boy do to help her win back Holland?

The illustrations to this story were suggested by various pictures painted by the Flemish artist, Jan Van Eyck (1390-1440). He and his brother, Hubert, were the earliest great painters of the Netherlands and lived at the court of Jacqueline's father, Count William of Holland, until he died, when they went to Duke Philip of Burgundy.

He wished to follow his pleasures all day, nor would he worry his head over any affairs of state. Worse than that, he delighted in mocking his wife by openly showing himself to be the friend of her foes. In spite of all this, however, Jacqueline would not be daunted. If her husband was naught but a booby, why then she would start out herself to recover her lost domains. She would take Dordrecht, where her uncle, John-without-Mercy, had now established himself. In this undertaking, she was promised help from Brabant, and depending on that aid, she marched boldly up to the very walls of Dordrecht, as self-reliant as any youth before the hard-headed John. But in the moment of crisis, those from Brabant did not come, she was forced to withdraw her troops, and her expedition failed. So Jacqueline had only three cities in Holland left faithful to her cause, to-wit: Gouda, Delft and Schiedam. And at this time her uncle John married a cousin of the Emperor, who straightway proclaimed his new kinsman to be Count of Holland and Zeeland in place of the Lady Jacqueline.

Now there was no man in Europe who more truly enjoyed looking on at the troubles in Holland than another cousin of Jacqueline's, Philip, the Duke of Burgundy. Philip understood very well how to fish in troubled waters. If there was only trouble enough in the provinces, he might drop in his own line, and perchance pull out the whole of the Netherlands on his hook! Aye, he was next of kin to the girl and her uncle, John. He might yet find the way to snatch the Netherlands for himself. He bided his time and waited, like a spider in the center of his web.

And while the Hooks and the Cods were quarreling and flying at each others' throats in Holland, the good works of peace to which men should have devoted themselves were altogether neglected. The building of roads, the care of dikes,—did men stop to think of such matters? No, and no again! Sad were the consequences.

In November, 1421, a violent storm from the northwest, forced the sea over the dikes and dams into the meadows near Dordrecht. Strongholds, castles, churches, all were washed away. Seventy-two villages were flooded, and when the waters receded, only fifty appeared again. Twenty-two had been lost; and for more than a hundred years, church spires and high walls could be seen, rising from the lake that remained on the land. Not until centuries had passed, did the water vanish entirely and leave those low-lying green meadows which today are called the Biesbosch.

But amid all this sadness and misery, due to such foolish neglect, the Hollanders never left off quarreling. And Jacqueline in her sorrow, knew not which way to turn. Her husband had deserted her, mocked at and betrayed her. On all sides she was beset by enemies, and ever the prey to men determined to steal her inheritance from her. One day she secretly set sail from Hainault and crossed the channel to England, to be received with royal honors at the court of Henry V. And there the young girl, so lonely and oppressed, saw Henry's brother, Humphrey, the handsome young Duke of Gloucester. And Jacqueline lost her heart. She could think of nothing but Humphrey,—so noble, so true the young man appeared in her eyes. Never before had her heart been consulted when her parents arranged a marriage. For the first time in her life, she inwardly glowed with a true and tender affection. So the wedding bells rang once again and she and Humphrey were married. "Now," she thought, "I have found a man whose love is real and true." But how could the church, in spite of her love, call such a marriage binding, when the ugly Duke John, alack, was still alive in Brabant?

Right speedily, the young couple came back to Holland, whereon

Duke Philip of Burgundy pretended to be in a rage because his cousin had married when her husband was still alive. In reality he was angry only because he feared she had found at last a true and sturdy defender, —and he challenged the Duke of Gloucester to meet him in a duel. Moreover, the Codfish party set about at once to stir up all the trouble they could, and make things as hard as possible for Humphrey, Duke of Gloucester.

And what went on then in the heart of the handsome Humphrey? The truth of the matter was that Humphrey was no better than those other rogues who had turned a greedy eye toward Jacqueline's possessions. He had married her to become the Lord of her rich domain, and for no other reason whatever. Therefore, as soon as he perceived that her people did not receive him with open arms, that her cousin Philip had challenged him to a duel, and that he should have to fight if he wished to possess her dominions, he was ready to desert her at once. He was called home, he said, to quell an uprising in England. Politely he made his excuses, and forthwith he departed, never to return to Holland.

Poor little Jacqueline, once again deserted in the midst of powerful enemies, sad at heart for the wound to her love, one girl against a host of men. Philip of Burgundy followed her into Hainault, the province always most faithful to her, and laid siege to her at Mons. In vain did Jacqueline appeal to Humphrey to return with reinforcements, and save her from her foes. Humphrey paid no heed, he was through with her forever. So at last Mons was forced to surrender, and the little Lady Jacqueline became Duke Philip's prisoner. Off she was packed to Ghent to be shut up in the castle.

Sad were the days for Jacqueline in her lonely prison in Ghent. And then came news to her that the Duke was planning to take her to Lille to lock her up for life. Secretly she sent messages begging for help to certain good friends in Holland. In answer to her plea, two gallant noblemen, Messires Spiring and Aalburg, decided to set her free. Making their way to Ghent, they gained admission to the Countess and told her the plans they had laid. One evening when the guards were eating their evening meal, Jacqueline and her maid dressed themselves in men's clothes and crept from their apartments. Down secret halls and byways they sped, until they were outside the castle.

At the foot of the castle walls, the two noblemen had horses ready, and when the four had mounted, they rode away for their lives. All night long they rode, but as the day was dawning they came safely into Breda.

And in those days, Jacqueline's husband, John of Brabant, and her

uncle, John of Bavaria, died. Then the Hook party raised its head everywhere in the land. The Cods had sported themselves long enough, without being caught, in the troubled waters of Holland. Let them now beware the Hooks! Jacqueline, at the head of a numerous army, defeated the Cods, near Alfen on the Rhine. And now that her husband was dead, she hoped with all her heart that Humphrey would return and make their marriage legal. She longed for him again. But Humphrey would still have none of her. He settled that question forever by wedding a wife in England.

Thus Jacqueline was left more than ever alone, and at the mercy of the most powerful of her foes. For this was the time when the spider, Duke Philip of Burgundy, determined to spring on his helpless prey. Since John of Bavaria was gone, Philip was the next male heir to Jacqueline's fair lands. He pounced down upon her at once, with tremendous, staggering force.

Threatened on all sides, bereft of hope, deserted by everyone who should have been her protector, Jacqueline decided at last to end the hopeless struggle. She had fought through long years with dauntless high spirit and courage, but this was too much. She renounced her power. Let the duke rule her lands as guardian. She kept only her title of Countess and a slender income in money. And so the sly duke had his way. In 1428 the House of Bavaria ceased to rule over Holland, Zeeland and Hainault, which fell to the house of Burgundy, by whom they were one day to be handed over to the ugly power of Spain.

Lady Jacqueline put the best face possible on the matter, and went without complaint, to take up her residence at the Hague. Some centuries before, the Hague had been merely a hunting lodge of the counts of Holland, but since the year 1250, and the days of Count William II, the castle in the Binnenhof had been a princely residence, enclosed by moats and approached by drawbridges. Here Lady Jacqueline made her home.

Meantime, her cousin, Duke Philip, lived in the utmost splendor. As Duke of Burgundy, he owed allegiance to the King of France, but his court was far more magnificent than that of his liege lord, the King. With Philip, all was luxury and show, glitter and brilliance, pageant and display, and to his court flocked the greatest of men, the greatest of artists, till the Flemish School of Painters spread his fame throughout the world.

When Jacqueline was a little girl, her father had once given her a beautiful Book of Hours, adorned with gay-colored paintings by the brothers, Jan and Hubert Van Eyck. This was the child's best loved book. How happy she had been to turn its handsome pages and look at the lovely pictures, and her father, Count William, had done his best to encourage the brothers Van Eyck, in their beautiful work of painting. But during the dark days of struggle, Jan and Hubert deserted the court of Jacqueline and went over to that of Duke Philip, where they added their brilliance to the glory surrounding his name. In the very days when Jacqueline had been shut up in her prison at Ghent, they were working near her, enlarging the fame of Duke Philip by painting *The Adoration of the Lamb* in the fine Cathedral of that old city. And Duke Philip was called by his henchman, Philip the Good, though what he had done to deserve such a name, none can say, unless he earned the name of Good by being surpassingly bad.

Now and then Jacqueline made a trip through her former realm, and it chanced that on one such occasion she fell in with a certain noble-man, Lord Chevalier Frank Van Borselen, whom Philip had appointed Governor of Holland and Zeeland. Now Van Borselen should have been the enemy of Jacqueline. Was not he a Cod and she a Hook? Nevertheless, she found him a gracious gentleman, full of a noble sweet-ness. And what, perchance, did he think of the charming little lady, so unfortunate and so fair? When she entered the reception hall of his castle, she saw the old stone walls and thick oaken doors decorated to greet her. Here hung green garlands of willow boughs, encircling the letter "D."

"And what does the letter D stand for?" the Lady Jacqueline asked.

"It means 'dyn'," Van Borselen answered. "I am 'dyn'," which is old Dutch for saying in familiar endearing fashion: "I am thine."

Lady Jacqueline blushed with pleasure.

"And what do the willow boughs mean?" she inquired. Now the word for willow in Dutch is very much like the word for willing, and Van Borselen answered:

"The willow boughs mean that I am thy willing servant."

How sweet were those words to the heart of the Lady Jacqueline, who had found in her short young life so few willing servants.

And the end of the matter was this—Van Borselen lost his heart to the fair unfortunate lady, and secretly they were married, a real marriage of love after all those years of grief. But O! what did happen when Philip heard news of the wedding! When Philip found out that the governor whom he had set over the provinces of Holland and Zeeland, had married the Countess of those lands, there was a pretty to-do, and that can well be imagined.

"Now," Philip thought, "those two will rise up together, and wrest the provinces from me!" So he sent off craftily and seized Van Borselen. He dragged him away from Jacqueline and shut him up in prison. It was a painful blow to one who had known in her life so little true affection. And now the time had come when Jacqueline valued Van Borselen more than aught else in the world. In hot haste, she mounted her palfrey and rode off to Duke Philip. If he would give back her husband, let him ask of her whatsoever he chose. She would yield him anything he might ask. To these anxious, wifely entreaties, Duke Philip answered that he would set Van Borselen free on one condition only. Jacqueline must give up to him even her titles as Countess of Holland, Zeeland, Hainault and Friesland. Under such conditions, so sorely pressed, what could a young wife do? She could only bow her head and consent. Let Philip take all she had, if he would but set Van Borselen free and let him come home again.

And now Philip had succeeded in each detail of his scheme. He had stripped his cousin completely of everything she possessed. Thus he became Lord of all the Netherlands. Flanders and Artois he had inherited; Namur he had bought; Brabant he had seized, together with Limburg, Antwerp and Mechlin; and now he got Holland, Zeeland, Hainault, and the title of Lord of Friesland.

In that very year, too, Philip's son, Charles, was born,—Charles the Bold, a tempestuous little fellow, who was to fight scores of battles and nearly ruin his dukedom by trying to make it a kingdom, independent of France. It was that passionate little lad who was to be the father of Mary of Burgundy, she who passed the Netherlands over to Austria by marrying the Emperor Maximilian, and became the mother of Philip the Fair, who continued the passing on of the Netherlands from one foreign power to another, by wedding the heiress of Spain, and leaving what had once been Jacqueline's provinces to his son, Charles V and the tyranny of Spain.

As to Jacqueline, in those days, thank God, she found happiness at last. Van Borselen loved her dearly and for herself alone. Though she had neither titles nor provinces now, he cherished her tenderly and loved her with all his heart. In the Castle of Teylingen in South Holland, they lived all the rest of their days, merry and content.

The Glorious, Joyous and Heroic Adventures of Tyl Ulenspiegel

Tyl, the Clown

TYL ULENSPIEGEL was a jolly fellow, a master of pranks and merry words. He wandered about the countryside to fairs and markets, praising what was good and beautiful and making sport of vanity

This picture was suggested by a painting by one of the earliest great Flemish artists, Peter Brueghel (about 1525-1570).

112

and conceit. Whenever market day came around in Middleburg or Bruges, there were shoemakers and tailors, each in his separate stall, there were the miesevangers from Antwerp (they that snare tomtits at night with the aid of an owl) there were rascally dog traders and vendors of breast-pads and doublets, all shouting their wares with every trick of the trade; and there, likewise, was Tyl, always playing the clown.

Tyl said he would show people their faces in a glass, and he set up, inside his booth, a great wooden frame with a curtain behind it, as though it had been a mirror. Then a swarm of country folk crowded in, expecting a merry jest. When there came along a swaggering dandy,

ready to part with a copper for the privilege of seeing his face, Tyl himself popped up from behind the frame, posing with the same lordly air and tilt of the nose, and pretending to be the reflection of the dandy who stood before him. Then the people roared with laughter, for that Tyl had showed the fellow how ridiculous was his conceit. And Tyl could frown like the ugliest Mr. Grim. He could make a saucy face to match any village lass, he could look stupid as the stupidest yokel, he could draw down his mouth most holily, like the primmest Better-than-Thou. But when a sweet young maid came by, innocent and lovely, or a little old lady, wrinkled of face, but with the freshness of spring in her heart, he would not show his own face at all, but would stick up in the frame a lovely bouquet of flowers. Thus he showed people their faces and their inmost hearts as well. And the crowd laughed and loved him and called him Tyl Ulenspiegel or Owlyglass.

But, though the people laughed, those were sad days in the country where Tyl was born. Those were the days when Flanders and the Low-Lands were ground down beneath the heel of Spain, when the Emperor Charles V had a greedy eye turned ever towards their powerful merchant cities. Those Dutchmen had more golden ducats than all the grandees of Spain, than all the princes of Germany, or the Indians of the New World, and Charles was determined to help himself, whenever he chose, to their treasures. But the sturdy Dutch cities were none too willing. They would not give him their ducats! They held their heads too high! They thought their own thoughts on government; they thought their own thoughts on religion, and in neither case did their thoughts agree in the least with those of the Emperor Charles. Bah! He vowed to make over to suit his own will the government and the religion of those stiff-necked Dutch burghers. Then many a good man or woman, yes, many a young lad or lassie suffered dire punishment for daring to defy him.

Now Tyl was a valiant fellow. He spoke out his mind concerning the Emperor Charles. Tut, tut! This was too bold of Tyl. Before he knew it, the Emperor's henchmen had shut him up in a dungeon, and then packed him off to Rome, sternly commanding him not to return until after a year and a day.

As Tyl tramped sadly along the roads and pathways of the world. it chanced that he met a donkey. The beast, which was harnessed with leather and studs of brass, its head ornamented with tassels and plumes of scarlet wool, was prancing about a bit, and a crowd of old women stood around, each telling the other what a dangerous monster he was.

"The impish creature's bewitched!" cried one. "Wasn't his master a wicked magician, who vanished in a cloud of smoke? That ass is a danger to our town and all the people in it!"

"Alack," cried a second old lady. "He kicks with his hind legs and brays in such fearful fashion! It is a shame and a pity that no man can be found to deliver the city from him!"

"If I were a man, I should have more courage," a third old lady cried. "I should go straight up and seize him by the bridle."

But, notwithstanding all this brave talk, the donkey had only to kick up his heels or flick his sides with his tail, to send the old women running away with cackling cries of terror.

"Only an angel could save us from such a monster," they cried.

Now Ulenspiegel could not help laughing at the sight.

"This bewitched beast," said he to himself, "is a sprightly ass, without a doubt, and a good goer. What if I were to take him for my own and so save the distressed city?"

Without another word, Tyl got a feed of oats and offered them to the donkey. In enjoyment of these viands, the donkey grew as docile as a lamb, and permitted Tyl to jump on his back, to turn him first to the north, and then to the east. When Tyl had thus ridden off from the old dames a little way, he turned around, raised his cap in a courtly manner and waved it like a conqueror. The women, open-mouthed with amazement, fell on their knees before him. And that evening they told in the town how an angel in a felt hat, trimmed with a pheasant's feather, had appeared to take away the magician's donkey and save the good people from him.

Ulenspiegel went his way through the green fields, where cows grazed at their ease or lay resting in the sunshine. And the ass was a good ass, and Ulenspiegel called him Jef. Thus it went day after day, and Jef could eat thistles by the roadside, but Tyl was often hungry. It seemed that his pockets had holes. Whenever he got a penny, alack. how soon it vanished!

"I don't know why it is," cried Tyl, "that money doesn't like me. when I am so fond of money!"

At last, his stomach empty as a drum, he came to the palace of the Landgrave of Hesse. Now Tyl had learned how to paint from strolling artists who came to the fairs where he played the clown, and he begged the Landgrave of Hesse to let him paint his portrait. Then the Landgrave, who was a jolly prince, treated him to a meal like a wedding feast, and paid him a hundred florins in advance to paint his portrait, with that of Madame the Landgravine, and all their lords and ladies, their captains and officers of state.

The next day Tyl asked the Landgrave to let him see those persons whose likenesses he was to paint. First there came the Duke of Luneburg, commander of the Infantry of the Landgrave. He was so monstrously fat through stuffing himself with food that he waddled when he walked and looked like nothing so much as a goose.

"When you paint my portrait," he whispered to Ulenspiegel, "see that you take off half my fat. If you don't I'll have you hung!"

Next came a noble lady, too lazy to stand erect, who had grown as stooped-over and round-shouldered as a monkey.

"Sir painter," said she. "Unless you paint me straight and erect, I'll have you drawn and quartered!"

Third, appeared a young maid-of-honor, fresh and fair, save that once she had got in a fight and lost three upper teeth.

"If you don't paint me smiling," said she, "and showing a perfect set of teeth, I'll have you chopped into little bits!"

And so it went with all the court. At last Tyl was left alone with the Landgrave.

"My friend," said the Landgrave. "Let me warn you. If you do not paint each one of my courtiers exactly as he is, I will have your head cut off as if you were a chicken!"

"Here's a fine to-do," thought Tyl. "I'm to be drawn and quartered,

117

chopped into small bits, and hung by the courtiers if I do not leave out all their blemishes and paint them fair and handsome, and I'm to have my head cut off by the Landgrave, if I do not paint them exactly as they are. I should do better to paint no portraits at all!''

So he had a curtain hung across the bare wall where he was to paint the pictures; then he shut himself up in the room, with his three apprentices and considered the matter. Well, it was only secondly that he was a painter! First of all, he was a merry fellow, who went through life praising the good and beautiful and making sport of vanity and conceit. Here was conceit in plenty and no doubt whatever about it. It was plain that this was no job for a painter; it was a job for a clown.

For sixty days, thereafter, Tyl and his apprentices remained in that room, and were served with the best of viands, but no one knew what they did, nor was any one permitted to poke so much as the tip of his nose in the chamber. As time went on, the Landgrave grew more and more impatient. At last he commanded: '' Show me the pictures at once!''

''Very well,'' answered Tyl, ''but pray have the kindness not to draw back the curtain until you have summoned the court!''

Soon lords and ladies and captains all sat before the curtain, each eager to see his own face. But Ulenspiegel said:

''Ladies and gentlemen, behind this curtain I have painted to the best of my abilities, all the beauty that I have seen in your faces. It will be quite easy for each of you to recognize himself. But know this,—all that are of noble blood, shall behold my paintings and rejoice, but if there be among you any whose parents were poor and lowly, such an one will see nothing but a blank wall!''

With that, he drew back the curtain. And what was before the court, save a bare, blank, empty wall? For Tyl had spoken truly,—all the beauty he had seen in their vain and selfish faces, was nothing, and so he had painted nothing. But who of that proud court was going to admit that he could not see the portraits? Who was going to let it appear that his family was poor and humble? They all made believe they could recognize the various faces and pointed themselves out to one another, though each was secretly ashamed because he saw nothing at all. And the fat old Duke of Luneburg was the biggest goose among them, for he insisted, more loudly than the rest, that he could see himself in the place of honor, by the right hand of his Lord.

Suddenly the court jester jumped three feet in the air and jangled his bells.

''Take me for a villain,'' he cried, ''a low-born, villainous villain, but

I verily will affirm and assert and declare with trumpets and fanfares that here I see a wall, a blank, white wall, and nothing but a wall, so help me God!"

At that Tyl took three strides toward the door, crying:

> *"When fools begin a-talking,*
> *'Tis time for wise men to be walking!"*

And he would have walked out of the palace in a hurry had not the Landgrave stopped him.

"Begone!" he cried. "And never dare show your face again in Hesse, under pain of instant death!"

Nevertheless, even as he spoke, the Landgrave was secretly shaking with laughter at the joke Tyl had played on his vain and foolish courtiers, and, unknown to all the rest, he slipped into Ulenspiegel's hands, fifteen golden florins. So Tyl was off on his donkey, holding his head up high, the pheasant's feather in his cap wagging joyously in the breeze.

He did not intend to return to Hesse, you may be sure of that! He knew too well what sort of welcome would greet him. But on his way home from Rome, he chanced all unwittingly, to cross once again the borders of that fair land, and he lay down in the shade of a tree to take forty winks while Jef beguiled himself with thistles. As he slept, who should come along but the Landgrave himself with a retinue headed by the fat Duke of Luneburg? Tyl awoke to find that great goose loudly demanding: "Hang the villain at once!"

"Take him prisoner," said the Landgrave.

Now Tyl was in a tight place. What but his wits could save him? No man could avoid arrest in Hesse unless he fled to his home. There, indeed, he was safe, for the law of Hesse said that no man might be taken prisoner between the four posts of his home. But alack, how should a poor fellow whose home was a donkey's back have four posts to flee to?

Suddenly Tyl was struck with a bright idea. Seizing Jef, he threw the donkey over on his back and sprang upon his belly, while the four feet of the overturned creature stuck up straight in the air about him.

"I crave the law, my Lord Landgrave!" he cried.

"The law!" thundered the Landgrave. "What law? you have defied my command and returned to Hesse. You are worthy to be hanged."

"But," cried Tyl, pointing solemnly to the four legs of his donkey, which stuck up absurdly around him. "You see I am within the four posts of my home, and the law of Hesse says, 'No man shall be taken prisoner so long as he is between the four posts of his home'!"

At this, the Duke of Luneburg began to rage, but the Landgrave

burst out into loud guffaws of laughter. And once again Tyl went free with a pocket full of florins.

Tyl and Philip II of Spain

Now about this time, Philip Sour-face, that is to say Philip II, son of the Emperor Charles, came to visit his future estates of Flanders, Brabant, Hainault, Holland and Zeeland. His face was cold, his manner stiff, his gray eyes bitterly gloomy. While tournaments, jousts and feasts went on, he was never seen to laugh.

And by what right, pray tell, was Philip the Spaniard, Lord of Flemings and Dutchmen, lord of a race so different from his? Ah, in those days, a land and all its people were but as so much lifeless gold, to be handed over, as a wedding gift, with a bride to her new-wed bridegroom. Philip's great grandfather, Maximilian, Emperor of Austria and Germany, had been given the whole of Burgundy, which then included the Netherlands, along with his wife, Mary of Burgundy; and his grandfather, Philip the Handsome, had increased their immense possessions by acquiring the whole of Spain with his wife Joanna, the daughter of Ferdinand and Isabella. It was due to marriages that Philip was heir to so vast a kingdom; it was due to marriages that the Netherlands belonged to his father, Charles V, and would soon belong to him.

At length, in his journeys, Philip came to Antwerp, where twenty-three triumphal arches had been erected to do him honor. The city expended hundreds of thousands of guilders on these arches, and on the rich uniforms of lackeys, burghers and merchants. There were to be seen the funniest of Dutch and Flemish jesters, the Prince of Joy from Dordrecht, riding on a pig; the King of Fools from Middleburg, who drove a horse by its tail, the Fool's Ship from down Limburg way, full of funny fellows in calfskins or donkeyskins, who played pranks and jokes with all kinds of innocent foolishness, but sober and gloomy Philip remained. He never once laughed nor smiled.

At night came the Margrave of Antwerp, the burgomasters, the captain and the deacons together to find something which could make Philip laugh. Then was brought to them news of the jester Tyl, who by now had arrived at Hertogenbosch in the duchy of Brabant. Post haste, they sent off for him in the hope that he could make Philip smile.

"Well," said Tyl, scratching his head. "If you want to amuse the King, I'll tell you what I will do,—I will fly!"

So the feast-heralds, mounted on beautiful horses covered with crimson velvet, rode through the streets, the market-places, and squares of Antwerp, beating the drum and blowing their horns. Thus they announced that Ulenspiegel, the fool from Hertogenbosch, was going to fly in the air at the quay, in the presence of King Philip and his respectable, high and noble court.

That day Ulenspiegel rode through the city on his donkey which was led by a footman ringing a cowbell. Tyl was dressed in a costly crimson silk garment which the city council had given him, and for head covering he wore a crimson silk cap with two donkey's ears from each of which tinkled a little bell. At the pointed elbows of his sleeves, and from the top of his long pointed boots, likewise hung golden bells.

Now a magnificent dais had been erected on the quay for the King, and when Ulenspiegel arrived, he left his footman and his donkey in the street, and, entering a house opposite the King's dais, he climbed through a window out on the gutter.

There he sounded all his little bells with a merry clamor and when every one was still to watch him, he stretched his arms out wide as if he were going to fly. Every spectator held his breath. But just at the very

121

moment when they expected to behold him quit the gutter entirely and launch himself in the air, what did Tyl do? He did not fly at all! Audacious clown! He bent far over the edge of the house and cried to King Philip below:

"Hey! I thought that I was the only fool in Antwerp, but I see the city is full of fools. If you had told me that you were going to fly, I would not have believed you; but a fool tells you that he will fly, and you believe him! How can I fly, having no wings?"

Some of the onlookers laughed, others were angry, but King Philip was stiff as a king of stone, and he never laughed nor smiled.

"It was not worth the trouble, to prepare all these amusements for such a sour face as that!" whispered the city councillors. So they gave Tyl three guilders, and off he went from the city.

Tyl and the Emperor Charles

By-and-by, Tyl came to the city of Oudenaarde, which a garrison of the Emperor Charles' hired soldiers was defending; for the King of France had sent troops into Flanders and they were laying waste the land like a swarm of grasshoppers. Now the Captain of the Emperor's hired soldiers was a rascal named Kornjuin, and he and his men stole chickens, ducks, pigeons, calves, and pigs, from the country-folk in a manner little less high-handed than that of the French. One day Kornjuin found Tyl asleep beneath a tree.

"What do you do for your living?" asked Kornjuin, awakening Tyl with a dig in the ribs.

"I dance on the rope," said Tyl. "I paint pretty faces, carve knifehandles, play the rumble pot, and blow the trumpet."

And this last he said because he had heard that on the castle of Oudennaarde the position of tower watchman was vacant.

"You shall be the trumpeter of the city," said Kornjuin.

Then he took Ulenspiegel to the top of the highest tower on the fortifications, and told him that he was to watch out for the enemy and blow his trumpet if he saw them coming.

This was all very well for the Emperor's soldiers, for thereafter they set themselves to feasting, and troubled themselves not at all about the enemy. Neither did they trouble themselves to give Ulenspiegel more than the barest necessities of food and drink, but they left the watching to him while they made merry below.

Now after some weeks which passed in this manner, Oudenaarde received news that the gracious Emperor Charles V was to visit the city with his high and noble retinue. On this occasion Ulenspiegel was given still less to eat and commanded to watch out still more sharply. He was to blow his trumpet the very moment His Majesty came into view, in order that the City Council might have time to ring the bells, get the fireworks ready, place the meats in the oven and open the casks of wine for the feasting. That he might perform his duty more certainly, the aldermen gave him a pair of spectacles.

One day when the wind blew from Brabant and the sky was clear, Tyl put on his spectacles and saw the Emperor coming.

But alack, Tyl was very empty in his stomach. He said to himself that he had been set up there to watch out against the coming of their enemy, the French. It was no business of his to blow his trumpet merely to awaken a false and silly display at the coming of an Emperor who beat and burned his people. It would do the Emperor good to fast for once in his life. Let the Emperor know what it felt like to have an empty stomach. So Tyl did not blow his trumpet.

Laughing and talking, the imperial party came on, steeds prancing, plumes waving, cloth-of-gold glistening. But as His Majesty drew nearer the gate, he was surprised and dissatisfied to find that no bells were ringing to announce his coming.

Meantime, a farmer, mistaking the newcomers for Frenchmen, came running into the city crying out: "Our foes are coming."

Whereat, the gatekeeper shut and locked the gate.

More and more angry, grew the Emperor, at hearing no bells nor thundering of cannon. In vain did he prick up his ears: he heard nothing but the chimes which played the half hour, and when he arrived before the city he found its gate fast closed. Then he fell to pounding imperiously on the panels, and the gentlemen of his retinue, angry like himself, demanded instant admission. But the gatekeeper, who stood up high on the fortifications, shouted to them that they should keep still, or he would send them a rain of bullets, which would cool their impatience a little. Grown altogether furious at this, His Majesty cried:

"Blind pig, don't you recognize your Emperor?"

To which the gatekeeper answered that pigs with the most gilt on, were usually the biggest pigs! Then didn't the Emperor rage?

"If you don't open this gate, I'll have you roasted alive!"

Such a noise as this at length brought an old soldier to the spot. He looked over the wall and cried to the gatekeeper:

"You are wrong! That is our Emperor! I know him well!"

Hearing this awful truth, the gatekeeper fell in a faint, while the soldier took the keys and opened the gate.

When he had entered the city, the Emperor demanded stormily why they had let him wait so long. The soldier explained the case, whereat

His Majesty sternly commanded that Kornjuin's troopers should appear at once before him. When they had come in all haste, he ordered them to ride before him, beating the tambourines, and playing the pipes.

Then at last the bells woke up,—one after another, they began to ring. With this escort and sufficient imperial noise, His Majesty arrived at the Market Place. Burgomasters and aldermen were having a meeting at that moment in the city hall; but Alderman Jan Guigelaer rushed into their midst, like one mad!

"Emperor Charles is here!" he shouted.

Frightened out of their wits, burgomasters, aldermen, and councillors, all ran out of the hall to greet the Emperor, while their boys went scurrying around the city to prepare the fireworks, to open the casks and to put the capons on the fire.

Then the Emperor asked the burgomasters if they did not deserve to be hanged for lack of respect to their sovereign lord.

The burgomasters answered that they deserved this, indeed, but that Ulenspiegel, the tower watchman, deserved it more; he had been put on the tower to watch for His Majesty's coming, and he had been given spectacles, extra good spectacles, with which to watch. Yet he had not blown his trumpet!

"Hang the wretch!" cried the Emperor.

So they brought Ulenspiegel and dragged him along by the collar to the gallows. There he was hoisted on a ladder and the hangman put the rope around his neck. But the common folk who loved Tyl and thought his offense too small to merit such punishment, cried out: "Mercy! Mercy for Ulenspiegel!"

At this, the Emperor lifted his hand and spake pompously as if to impress them all with a sense of the limitless power of him whom they had failed sufficiently to honor.

"I am the Emperor! All power on earth is mine. Whatever I will, I do! If this good-for-nothing can ask of me anything that I cannot do, I will let him live."

Then the women wept and said:

"Poor boy! He must die, for the Emperor can do anything!"

Nevertheless, they cried one and all: "Speak, Ulenspiegel! Speak!"

Ulenspiegel thought a moment and then he answered solemnly:

"This one thing only will I ask,—that His Majesty come and kiss me on that mouth with which I cannot speak Dutch!"

Hearing this unexpected answer, the Emperor burst into laughter.

"I cannot do what you ask," said he. "Therefore you will not be hanged."

Nevertheless he sentenced the burgomasters and aldermen of the city, to wear spectacles on the back of their heads for six months, so that, "if those of Oudenaarde cannot see in front, they can at least see behind," he said. And, by imperial decree, the spectacles are still on the coat of arms of that city.

The Adventures of Tyl and Lammie Goodfellow

Now soon after this, Emperor Charles grew weary of the burden of ruling his mighty empire, so in the year 1555, he turned the crown with great ceremony over to Philip, and, putting off all his splendor, he went to live in quiet in a monastery. Then was Philip King alone, and the throne, and the crown, and the robes of state, and the royal orb were his. And this was the worse for Flanders and the Low-lands. For Philip Sour-face was as obstinate as a mule, and he thought that his own will ought to dominate the whole world as though it had been the will of God. But the Dutchmen would neither surrender to him their independence of mind, nor disgorge to him their ducats. The flame of resistance began to burn and run through all the land. And William of Orange, called William the Silent, with the Counts of Egmont and Horn.

and other powerful nobles of Flanders and the Low-lands, rose up to save their people from the direful power of Spain.

When things came to such a pass Philip set sail from Flushing and returned once more to Spain, nor did he ever again set foot on the land that had defied him. But he made his sister, Margaret of Parma, governor in his stead and he left 4,000 Spanish troops to enforce his will on the land.

One fine day three hundred nobles of the Netherlands, led by Henry of Brederode and Louis of Nassau, the gallant brother of William the Silent, went to Margaret of Parma in her palace at Brussels, to entreat her to use her influence with King Philip to soften the burdens, indignities, and punishments which he had heaped upon them. Frightened at sight of so large a throng, Margaret trembled, but one of her followers, Berlaymont, Stadtholder of Namur and member of the Council of State, attempted to reassure her. Looking about at the nobles of the Netherlands, who were dressed with conspicuous plainness and carried no weapons whatever, he cried with great scorn:

"Have no fear, my lady, they are naught but a pack of beggars!"

"Naught but a pack of beggars!" That night at a banquet at the home of Henry of Brederode, the young nobles adopted the name of Beggars. And the Prince of Orange, with the Counts of Egmont and Horn, who dropped in on the revelry, joined the merry scene, and drank the beggarmen's health. Thenceforward, it became the fashion for patriots to wear beggars' garb with a medal around their necks, and to call themselves "Beggar-men!"

Then Philip recalled Margaret of Parma as governor of the Netherlands and sent to replace her, the Duke of Alva, a man as hard as iron, as hard as the iron of captured cannon with which he caused to be made a statue of himself! In no time at all, the Iron Duke had cut off the heads of the Counts of Egmont and Horn, and William of Orange was forced to flee into Germany for safety.

Having lost all he had in the Low-lands, William sold his gold and silver, gathered together an army and came back again into Holland. And Tyl fell in with an old friend, Lammie Goodfellow, who was huge as an ox, but peaceable as a lamb, whence he had his name of Lammie, and the two joined the Beggarmen, though Lammie had never before attacked a single living thing save a chicken, or a goose.

Thenceforward by day and night, the fires of the Beggarmen were to be seen flaring up or dying down in the woods and the peasants brought them such bread and bacon as they could.

"Look at these fine fellows, Lammie!" cried Ulenspiegel. "Fierce and talkative, resolute and proud, they wander through the woods. And they are armed with hatchets and halberds, with long swords, arquebuses, pikes, lances, crossbows. Long live the Beggarmen!"

Thereafter, Ulenspiegel applied himself most diligently to his duties as a soldier, worked his arquebus most skilfully, and kept his eyes and ears wide open. But as to Lammie, despite that he was so big and powerful as to make men tremble before him, he felt ill at ease in warfare, because of the softness and gentleness of his heart.

Now it came to pass that the attempts of the Prince of Orange and his friends to gain a stronghold in the Netherland, were all in vain. By land they failed and the fate of the Low-lands looked dark, indeed. Then one day, William the Silent said to Tyl and Lammie:

"I would have you go for me to North Brabant, Gelderland, Overyssel, and the North of Holland, telling the people everywhere that, although we have failed on land, we will yet continue the struggle for freedom by sea! On your journey, count those worthy of your trust who answer the song of the lark with a warlike cockcrow."

So Tyl dressed himself in a short cloak and a shabby doublet and hose made after the Spanish fashion, and with plumed cap on his head, he and Lammie departed from camp.

Many a day they wandered astride their donkeys, Jef and Jan, and many adventures befell them, but at last they drew nigh to Maastricht. Not far from the town they came to a farm. There Ulenspiegel whistled like a lark, and from inside the house there answered the sound of a warlike cockcrow. After that a jolly-looking farmer appeared at the door to greet them.

Soon the ham was crackling in the frying-pan and the sausages likewise. And the boys and girls of the farm came one after another and thrust their noses into the half-open door to gaze on Lammie in wonder at the amount that he could eat. But the farmer said to Tyl:

"You cannot go to Maastricht, for the Duke's army is camped in front of the town and around it on every side."

With that, he conducted his visitors up into the loft whence they could see the standards of the enemies' cavalry and infantry moving about in the distance over the plain.

Nevertheless, Tyl said: "Fear not! I have a plan to get through the enemies' lines and to take with me some of these good lads of yours who are longing to get to the river, and so to the sea to join the Sea-Beggars. I am going to pretend that I am a bridegroom. You shall furnish me with a pretty bride and then you shall see what will happen."

So all the men put on their best clothes, their doublets and hose of

127

velvet, and the great opperst-kleed over all. As for the women, their skirts were of black wool with broad stripes of black velvet thereon. Round their necks they wore white ruffs, their bodices were embroidered in gold, scarlet and blue, and their shoes had silver buckles.

At noon, while the sun shone down from a clear sky, and a fresh breeze was blowing, the wedding carriages started off, all decorated with paper flowers and wreaths of fir and holly. In the first cart were Tyl and Lammie and she, who pretended to be the bride. In the second, which was drawn by Jef and Jan, rode the musicians playing on drums and fifes, bag-pipes and shawms. Last of all, came two wagons loaded with wedding guests. Flags flying, and music playing, they rode up the highway to the town.

When the sentries saw them coming, they ran to the Duke and cried: "The enemy is at hand."

The Duke at once sent to warn the colonels and the captains, and himself ordered the army to be massed in battle array.

But as the carriages drew near, it was seen that they contained none but men and women, dancing and singing and playing most joyously on fifes and drums, on bagpipes and shawms.

When the procession had been brought to a halt, the Duke himself came up, attracted by the din that came from all those instruments. And he saw naught but a bride and bridegroom, covered with flowers. Then all the other peasants, both men and women, got down from the chariots, beginning to dance on the ground and offer food and drink to the soldiers. The Duke and his friends were much astonished at the simplicity of these peasants. Look how they sang and made merry when all around was an army ready for battle! And when the cavalcade moved off, far from holding them back, the soldiers in high good humor let off a volley of musketry in honor of the bride.

Thus they came in safety into Maastricht, whence the peasants made their way down the river Maas to the Sea-Beggars, while Ulenspiegel took counsel with agents of the Prince as to the best way of sending ships loaded with arms and munitions to the assistance of the fleet.

The Duke was not long in learning the trick which had been played upon him. Thenceforward, the Dutchmen sang:

> *"Bloody Duke,*
> *Silly Duke,*
> *Hast thou seen the Bride?"*

And whenever he made a mistake, his enemies cried:

> *"The Duke he can't see clearly;*
> *He has seen the Bride!"*

Now in those days Lammie and Ulenspiegel were walking along the banks of the Maas, near the town of Maastricht, and Lammie saw that Ulenspiegel gazed attentively at all the boats on the river. Suddenly he came to a stand before one, on the prow of which stood the figure of a mermaid. Then Ulenspiegel began to sing like a lark. A man appeared on the boat and answered with a cock-crow. At this, Ulenspiegel set up a noise like a donkey's bray, which the man immediately echoed with interest. And the two donkeys, Jef and Jan, laid back their ears and joined in the chorus. Then Tyl said to Lammie:

"This boatman is making mock of us and our good steeds. What do you say to going and attacking him in his boat?"

But sundry men and women, who were riding along the tow-path on the backs of the horses which pulled the barges, cried out in warning:

"If you don't want to be broken to bits, let this Stercke Pier bray at his ease. He is the strongest man in Maastricht."

"Ee-aw! Ee-aw! Ee-aw!" went the boatman.

But Ulenspiegel proudly answered the people:

"He's nothing to us,—your Peter the Strong! For however strong he is, we are stronger! See my friend Lammie here. He could deal with this man as though he were a gnat!"

"What's this you're saying, my son?" demanded Lammie, in alarm.

"The truth," answered Ulenspiegel. "And do not let your modesty contradict me. Your strength is famous far and wide."

"Ee-aw! Ee-aw!" went the boatman.

Then Ulenspiegel said aloud to the boatman:

"If you are Stercke Pier, I am Tyl Ulenspiegel. And these two here are our donkeys, Jef and Jan, and they know how to bray better than you do, for that is their natural way of talking."

"Ee-aw! Ee-aw!" scornfully cried the boatman.

So Tyl and Lammie dismounted from their donkeys, jumped into a little skiff, and steered straight for the boat. Tyl mounted to the deck by the help of a rope, and Lammie climbed up in front of him, puffing and blowing. Arrived on the bridge of the boat, Ulenspiegel leant down as if to lace his boots, and at the same time he spoke a word into the ear of the boatman, who straightway laughed and gave Lammie a curious look. Then he began to roar out at him every kind of insult, calling him a coward, and a huge lump of fat and names even worse than these.

It was midday. The workmen who labored on the dike and the road-menders and the builders of ships were about to take their repast of beans and boiled beef, which had been brought them by their women-folk or their children. All these came crowding to the shore, and began to laugh and to clap their hands at the prospect of a fight.

All of a sudden, Lammie threw himself like a mad bull upon the boatman, knocked him down, and began to beat him with all his might. And the boatman suffered himself to be thus dealt with, despite the fact that he was making a great pretense at resistance all the time. Then the men and women, who were watching the battle from the bank, were astonished and clapped their hands and exclaimed to each other: "Who would have thought that this fat man could be so fiery?"

"Beg for mercy!" cried Lammie, kneeling on his enemy's breast.

At this the boatman began to cough, and demanded mercy with a sign of his hand, whereat in generous fashion, Lammie picked him up. Straightway his adversary turned his back towards the onlookers, and stuck out his tongue at Tyl who was rocking with laughter to see Lammie proudly shaking the feather on his cap and walking about in triumph.

"Long live the conqueror of Stercke Pier!" cried the good folk on the shore. And the boatman, having made his peace with Lammie, said:

"Since you are men of valiant heart, knowing well the song of the lark, the bird of freedom, the warlike clarion of the cock, and the bray of the ass withal, come with me and I will show you what is cooking in my kitchen."

So saying, he led the way into the hold, where, removing certain planks from the floor, he disclosed great piles of guns and powder.

"Where am I to take these?" he asked of Tyl.

"To Emden, through the North Sea," said Ulenspiegel, "good Beggarman that you are!"

"The sea is big," said the boatman.

"Big for battle," said Ulenspiegel.

"God is with us," said the boatman.

"Who then can be against us?" cried Ulenspiegel.

When they had thus spoken, the boatman conducted Lammie and Ulenspiegel on deck with many words of cheer and good counsel. Then the two rowed to the bank, where they mounted their donkeys again.

"My son," said Lammie, as they ambled gently along, "pray tell me why did that man, strong as he is, allow me to beat him so cruelly?"

"To the end," answered Ulenspiegel, "that wherever we go, the fear of your prowess may go before us. That, indeed, will prove a more powerful escort than twenty landsknechts, for who would dare to measure his strength with Lammie, the mighty, Lammie, the conqueror, who overcame in sight of all beholders the famous Stercke Pier and threw him to the ground like a feather?"

"You say well, my son," said Lammie, drawing himself up proudly.

Then Lammie passed along the road, saluting right and left like a King, and the fame of his valor followed him from village to village and town to town. And Lammie let his beard grow to make him look the more fierce. And Ulenspiegel called him Lammie, the lion. But Lammie did not continue in his purpose regarding the beard longer than the fourth day, because the hairs of it began to tickle him. And he passed a razor over the surface of his victorious countenance, so that it appeared thereafter like his own face once more, round and full as the sun, ablaze with the flame of good nature.

So they wended along by the banks of river and canal, and everywhere the song of the cock answered the song of the lark. And wherever they went, they found that in the sacred cause of Liberty, weapons were being forged and armor furbished to be carried away in the ships that stood by along the coast.

The Sea Beggars

At last Tyl and Lammie came to Heyst-on-the-Dunes, and beheld a fleet of fishing boats that were come hither from Ostend and from Blankenberghe and Flushing. Filled they were with men-at-arms, the followers of the Beggarmen of Zeeland.

Then Lammie and Ulenspiegel went aboard one of the ships and

were carried to Emden and thence to Wieringen where their ship was hemmed in by the ice. For by now it was the month of February. Against the gray, bright sky the skeletons of the trees stood out in motionless outline. Their branches were covered, as it were, with cushions of snow, and the roofs of the cottages, likewise. Far and wide the fields were hidden under that wonderful white fleece.

Now all around the ship there was to be seen the most joyous sight imaginable,—men all clad in velvet, sledging and skating on the ice; and women skating, too, with skirts and jackets bordered with pearl and gold, and blue and scarlet. And the boys and girls came and went hither and thither, laughing and following one another in line, or two by two in couples, singing the song of love upon the ice, and running to eat and drink at the stalls decorated with flags, where one could buy all kinds of goodies,—oranges, and figs, and eggs, and heete-koeken, that is to say, pancakes, and hot vegetables flavored with vinegar. And all around them, the sailing sledges made the ice to resound under the press of their sharp runners. Then Tyl cried out to Lammie:

This picture was suggested by various paintings of the Dutch artist, Isaac Van Ostade (1621-1649), who loved to paint winter scenes and merry-makers on the ice. See page 156.

*"What action! What commotion! What a lot of noise!
My eyes are dazzled by it all! What crowds of boys!
There comes Harmen Hooghart, faster than them all,
He hooks his skate in Nanny's so the good girl takes a fall.
There comes that frail boy Jerrie, stumbling, skidding by,
The poor young bungler's skating with that tall Lizzie Vry.
I'm sorry for blue Agatha, so very cold she grows,
It's strange that no big icicles are hanging from her nose!
How proud is Melis with his girl,—they make a pretty pair,
And dirty Mary Slomps is with her grandpa there.
See those little dried-up men whizzing in a row,
One behind the other, just like geese, they go.
There's Johnny What-you-call-him, he shoves in one push-sled
His grandma, wife and children, besides his Auntie Gred.
Ah, how the farmers' sleighs go here and every way.
How our common folk and nobles all go sporting in the sleigh."

Translated from *An Ice Picture* by Gebrand Adriansen Brederoo, one of the greater Dutch poets (1585-1618).

When Spring came once again, the Beggarmen sailed away and joined the fleet of Messire Lumey de la Marck, the Hog of Ardennes, Admiral of Holland and Zeeland. And on April Fool's day, 1572, they played a joke on the haughty Spaniards; for they sailed up against Briel, at the mouth of the river Maas, and Briel surrendered to them, the first strong naval base to open its gates to the Beggars.

Now in the Flemish tongue, the word Briel signifieth "spectacles" and, to celebrate this event, the servants of Laughter in the Low-lands composed a ridiculous rhyme:

When April Fool's day came to vex,
The Duke of Alva lost his "Specs!"

Hearing how the Iron Duke had lost his specs, the burghers of Flushing likewise drove the Spaniards from their town. Then Veere in Zeeland, Enkhuisen, Alkmaar, Horn, Edam, Monnikendam, Leyden, Gouda, Dordrecht, Haarlem and many another city had courage to take the side of the Prince, and defy the power of Spain. And in solemn assembly united, the provinces of the Netherlands declared William of Orange to be stadtholder of the land.

So swept the resolute but fantastic band of Beggars along the placid estuaries of Zeeland, waking the quiet waters with their wild songs. And the sound of their voices was like the growl of the thunder of deliverance. And Ulenspiegel sang:

"Long live the Beggarmen! Loud beat the drum!
The Briel has fallen,
Flushing, too, the key to the Scheldt!
God is good, for Camp Veere is taken,
Taken the place where the guns of all Zeeland were stored!
Now cannon-balls, powder and bullets are ours,
Bullets of iron, bullets of brass,
God is with us—who then is against us?
The drum! Beat the drum!
Long live the Beggarmen! Beat the drum!"

And now it was Wintermonth, that is the month of wolves. Rain fell in the water like sharp needles. The Beggars were cruising on the Zuyder Zee. And Ulenspiegel had become commander of a vessel called The Briel, with Lammie risen to the glory of Chief Cook. Then the Admiral said to Tyl:

"I have to tell you, that the Spaniards of Amsterdam are planning to besiege Enkhuisen, but they have not yet left Amsterdam harbor and we are going to cruise in front of the Y, so that we can close it, and attack every boat that dares to show its hull in the Zuyder Zee."

So the fleet left and cruised in front of Amsterdam, and no ship could enter or leave the harbor unless the Beggars allowed it.

On the fifth day, however, the rain stopped and the wind blew colder; but those of Amsterdam still gave no sign of action.

Suddenly Ulenspiegel saw his friend Lammie, chasing a rascally cabin boy and waving his wooden spoon threateningly in the air.

"Lammie," said Tyl, "all is so quiet in Amsterdam, I fear they are up to something."

"I was thinking of that," said Lammie. "The water is freezing in the jugs; the chickens are as hard as wood; the sausages are white with frost; the butter is like stone, the salt is as dry as sand in the sun. That means we are going to have freezing weather."

"Then the water about us will be ice," said Ulenspiegel, "and the enemy can cross it on foot. They will come in large numbers with blunderbusses."

Forthwith, he was off to the Admiral's ship to tell him his fears, but the Admiral would not believe that Lammie had read the signs of the weather aright. Nevertheless, by sunset the sea was frozen over and smooth as a floor. Then the Admiral feared that those from Amsterdam would cross the ice and set fire to the ships. So he told the soldiers to keep their skates ready, in case they should have to fight, and he ordered the gunners to load the guns and keep the lunts burning.

But those of Amsterdam did not come.

Thus seven days passed. Towards evening of the seventh day, Tyl ordered that a good meal should be given his men. But Lammie said:

"We have nothing left to give them save hard-tack. Who will go ashore with me and seize some tasty provisions?"

"We cannot go ashore," replied Tyl. "The enemy might come."

"Friend," said Lammie. "Please remember that our last sausage was eaten yesterday. Now look at yonder lights ashore,—they are those of a rich homestead, well stocked with large and small cattle. Do you know who lives there? It is that skipper, Slosse, who betrayed eighteen of our innocent countrymen to the Spaniards so that they, by his fault, lost their heads. As the price of his treason, he received from the Duke two thousand florins and with this blood money he bought, like a real Judas, the homestead which you see before you. Give me twenty brave men and the traitor shall meet with justice, for my stomach says it is meal-time."

"I shall go myself," cried Tyl. "Who is for justice, follow me! Buckle on your skates and direct your way by yon bright star, which shines above the traitor's house.

135

..... So come, friends, skating and gliding, with the ax on the shoulder, led by the glimmering light of the moon.

..... The wind whistles and blows up the snow. In a ghostly winding sheet it swirls across the ice. Come, brave men!

..... You neither sing nor talk. Silently you go, straight toward the star; your skates are scratching the ice.

..... Who falls, arise at once. We are nearing the shore,—not a single human form on the white snow, not a single bird in the icy sky. Take off your skates.

..... And now we are near the house, hold your breath."

Ulenspiegel knocked on the door, the dogs barked. He knocked again; a window was opened and the farmer put out his head.

"Who are you?" he cried, but he saw no one save Tyl, for the others were hidden behind the barn.

"Messire Bossu summons you to Amsterdam," said Tyl.

"Where is safe-conduct?" asked the farmer, appearing at the door.

"Here," answered Ulenspiegel, pointing to his twenty bold Beggars. "You are the traitor, Slosse, who caught our comrades in a trap. Where is the bloodmoney that was paid you?"

Trembling all over, the farmer answered:

"I have no money in my house. All I have, I will give you."

But when the candles were lit, a Beggarman who stood near the fireplace, seized a flower pot, which was one of a row that adorned the shelf. Turning it upside down, he shook out a mass of ducats.

"There is the treasure," he said, pointing to the other pots.

And verily, he spake the truth, for when the pots were emptied, the Beggars counted ten thousand florins.

Then the farmer began to cry and to weep, and his men-servants and maid-servants, hearing him howl, came running to him in their night shirts. But the Beggarmen caught and bound the men-servants who would have defended their master, and Lammie cried:

"Traitor, where are the keys to your cellar, barn and sheepfold?"

"Impertinent thieves," shrieked the farmer, "you shall be hanged!"

Notwithstanding his howls, the Beggars ransacked the farmhouse, and seized what was needed for their men. Then they went skating back to the ships, the light halls of freedom.

"I am the cook," cried Lammie, leading the way; "I am the cook. Push the good sleds, loaded with food; drive with ropes the oxen, the pigs and the sheep. The pigeons coo in their cages; the capons look troubled in their pens! I am the cook. The ice cracks under the skates. We are near the ships. Tomorrow there shall be music, music in the

kitchen. Let down the pulleys! Draw up the cows and the oxen. There go the pork chops! Put them all in the hold, ducks, capons, geese, hens! The door is locked, I am the cook, the key is in my pocket. The Lord be praised in the kitchen! Long live the Beggarmen!"

Thus there was feasting for the Beggars, but even while they feasted, behold black crowds long the shore, shadowy forms with torches flashing and weapons gleaming among them.

The Admiral's orders were given on the instant. All fires were put out; sailors and soldiers lay down on their stomachs armed with axes. The canonneers with lunt in hand were on guard near the blunderbusses.

"Do you hear," said Tyl to Lammie in a low voice like the breath of a ghost. "Do you hear the voices of those from Amsterdam and their skates scratching on the ice? They go fast. You can hear them talk. They say: 'Those lazy Beggars are fast asleep. Ours is the treasure of Lisbon.' Do you see their ladders and their ugly faces?"

"Fire!" cried the Admiral of the Beggars.

A sound was heard like thunder, and loud cries on the ice.

"They run away," cried Tyl.

"Pursue them!" said the Admiral.

But the fugitives ran like rabbits. It was victory for the Beggars!

Still the Admiral's heart was troubled, for the ice showed no signs of melting and there might come another attack across that glistening floor. Then Lammie sprang on deck and said to Tyl:

"Take me to that Admiral, who did not want to believe you when you told him there would be freezing weather."

"Go without being taken," said Ulenspiegel.

So Lammie went off to the Admiral.

"Messire Admiral," said he, "may a humble cook tell you something?"

"Speak, my boy," said the Admiral.

"Sir," said Lammie, "if the great scholars who pretend to be astrologers could read the stars as well as I can read my sauces, they would tell you that it's going to thaw tonight. The water is thawing in the jugs, the fowls are getting soft; the sausage loses its coat of white frost; the butter becomes soft; the salt damp. Soon the ice will melt so no one can cross it, and we shall be safe, Sir Admiral. But you must sail away at once, for the thaw will not last."

By evening his words came to pass, and loudly Lammie rejoiced:

"The North Sea is high! The waves which enter the Zuyder Zee are breaking up the ice. See, in great pieces it explodes and falls against the ships! How it shines and glitters! And now there is water enough to float our largest vessel. Our ship spreads its sails like a bird of freedom and makes for the open sea. Ho, for the winds and the waves! And now we are safe in the port of Enkhuisen. The sea freezes again. We have sailed just in time. I am a prophet, and it is a favor of the Lord!"

And Ulenspiegel said: "We shall praise and thank Him."

And winter passed and summer came, and the Spaniards laid seige to Alkmaar. Three times they stormed the city and three times they were driven back, till at last they withdrew in sorry defeat from before those stubborn walls. Then there went out a great cry through all the Netherlands: "From Alkmaar begins the victory!" And so it was. From Alkmaar began the victory. And Alva went back to Spain and Requesens came to take his place. But the Sea-Beggars took Middleburg in Zeeland from under the very nose of Requesens. Through the wild waves went the Sea-Beggars, like lions through a wood. And winter passed and spring came once again.

The Siege of Leyden

Now it was May of the year 1574, and all eyes were turned toward Leyden, for in that year the Spanish General, Valdez, who had laid siege to the city to none effect in the autumn before, appeared for a second time and occupied his old forts, which the burghers had failed to destroy. Then were the citizens of Leyden shut up once more within their own fortifications with but a sorry supply of food and naught but a small corps of burgher guards as their defenders. Before them lay thousands of Spanish troops encamped upon the meadows; around them rose sixty-two redoubts bristling with cannon, all made ready to bombard the city walls. Little was there in their favor, save that they had as Burgomaster that stout old rebel, Adrian Van der Werff.

In those dark days, the hope of Van der Werff and his burghers lay in the justice of God and the tireless energy of William of Orange. Now William could raise no army large enough to defeat the Spaniards on land, but over in the North Sea, he collected his fleet of Beggars under command of Admiral Boisot. And Tyl trod the deck of his vessel, sad at heart, beholding clouds drift gently by and the sea all blue and sparkling about him, and he cried aloud to Lammie:

"Oh, Lammie, behold the lovely month of May. Ah! the bright blue of the sky and the blue of the sea! On shore the flowers are blooming, the chaffinches are singing in the trees and, O, the joy of the swallows! The very earth is in love. Yet is there no love in the heart of the tyrant. His clutch draws closer about our necks. Our two largest cities, Amsterdam and Haarlem, are already in his hands. If Leyden, likewise, should fall, what then would keep our comrades from utter despair? They would lay down their arms and yield up the struggle. We dare not let Leyden fall. On Leyden depends the salvation of Holland!"

But Lammie answered:

"Long live the Prince of Orange, the friend of our country! Under his command we shall yet carry bread and sausage to Leyden!"

Nevertheless, between the fleet and Leyden lay fifteen miles of rich Dutch meadows over which swarmed the Spanish host. How was William of Orange to get the food through the enemy's lines and into the starving city?

Month after month went by. The burghers were grimly enduring. Day by day, men, women, and children crept like shadows along the street. By the still canals, in the peaceful shade of the trees, they wended their way up to Hengist Hill, atop which stood an ancient tower, the only high spot in the city. From there they could look out across the fields and strain their eyes in hopes of catching some glimpse of relief coming out of the distance.

"What ho?" they cried to the watchman on the tower. "Do you see help coming?" And month after month the watchman could answer only, "I see naught but the enemy in the meadows below."

Then was there dull booming of cannon without, and pitiless hunger within. And in those days William of Orange said:

"Have we not men enough to drive the Spaniards out of the land and bring succor to starving Leyden? Then the sea itself shall come to the rescue! Cut the dikes and let in the waters over the meadows."

Forthwith, the dikes were cut. Ah! the sea had many times seemed an enemy to the people of the Low-lands. They and their fathers, and their fathers' fathers for generations before, had labored to force it back behind the dikes and wrest from its grasp their rich low-lying, green meadows. Yet now they looked to it as a friend and they cut the dikes and invited it in, careless what it should do to the meadows if only

WILLIAM OF ORANGE

it brought up the ships to Leyden.

But alack! it was still the summer season, a season of calm and sunshine, and, though the dikes were broken through, no storm-wind came with a giant's hand to hurl the waters over the land. Only little pools drifted gently in and lay peacefully on the meadows.

Nevertheless carrier pigeons flew into Leyden and bore to Adrian Van der Werff and his people that magic message from William:

"We have cut through the dikes!"

From every lip in Leyden went up a shout of thanksgiving! When the wind should blow strongly enough from the north and the west, the sea would rise, plunge over the broken dikes, and then,—ah, then! a thunderous, all powerful watery giant would come to the rescue of Leyden. Now the good folk of Leyden climbed to the top of Hengist Hill with real reason to hope.

"Watchman! Watchman, what see you now? Is the sea rising?"

But it was a long and weary time still that the watchman answered:

"I see only puddles in the fields far off nearest the sea!"

Sometimes the weary watchers beheld in the sky the rosy reflections of bonfires as some distant village illumined itself with flames to honor the progress of the fleet. Sometimes they heard far off the booming of the guns, but time passed and no help came.

Hope began again to die. Patience was tried to its utmost. Horses, dogs, cats and rats, the very grass by the roadside,—this was the food of the people of Leyden and even this was failing. Then Adrian Van der Werff went about among the burghers, trying to fire their faith anew, and keep warm the embers of hope. But there came a day when their courage fell to the lowest ebb. Dull of eye, they crowded together about the Burgomaster.

"Give up the city," they said. "We can hold out no longer!"

Then the staunch old Dutchman, standing, haggard, but imposing, beneath two ancient lime trees at the foot of the tall brick tower of St. Pancras Church, waved his broad-brimmed hat and cried:

"Give up the city? Never! Take my body and eat it if you will, but I shall not give up the city."

Brave words, old Adrian Van der Werff, and more powerful than hunger or cannon! The burghers of Leyden, sublime in their despair, spurned the summons to surrender, and set themselves anew to the terrible task of waiting. Every eye turned wistfully with each new day toward the weather vanes on the steeples. When would the wind change and blow in their savior, the sea?

But at last the slow-creeping autumn came. From the deck of his vessel, Tyl now beheld how the clouds went racing like mad things over the sky, while out at sea, the wild, white crests came surging up on the waves. And one day the burghers of Leyden rose to find that the wind had changed,—in the air was the strong salt smell of the sea. Great was the excitement within the walls, and the watchers thronged to Hengist Hill. From there they could see their deliverer coming,—the distant puddles grew into ponds, the ponds widened and joined themselves into a shallow lake. And then came night and the tempest. The sky was black with clouds, the wind raged and howled, the trees groaned and cracked. From the direction of the sea came an ominous murmur that

slowly grew and swelled to a roar. There it came, the sea, the mighty sea, a huge black wall of water, rolling, crashing, thundering. Over field and meadow it surged, washing all away that stood in its path, straight up to the walls of Leyden.

In the darkness lights were seen in the Spanish camp; wild confused cries were heard as the Spaniards awoke from their fancied security to see what was upon them.

Early in the morning of the third day of October, a small Dutch boy, straining his eyes in the dim gray light toward the largest of the Spanish forts, saw that it seemed deserted. Making his way across the watery meadows, he crept up alone to the fortification, and there he found to his joy, that it was as he had supposed,—the enemy had fled. In wild exultation he waved the news to his friends within the city. And what else did he find within the deserted camp? Still hanging above the embers of a smouldering fire, he found a brass pot full of savory stew, potatoes, carrots, onions and meat! Hutspot! Hutspot! What a feast for starving burghers! Sound the pipes, pipes of joy for the savory stew of hutspot!

And when dawn had progressed to broad daylight lo! the people of Leyden saw sailing toward them in motley array, the vessels of the Beggars. Straight over the fields of Holland they sailed, where the day before had been only green meadows. Amid half submerged trees and chimney stacks, on they came and on. And Ulenspiegel was there and Lammie too, and great was their joy and excitement.

Now many of King Philip's troops had been washed away by the flood, but some had taken to any rude craft they could find, and were floating about in the water. These Tyl and his comrades overturned and sent sprawling into the sea. So at last the Spaniards were put to rout! Along the road to the Hague, in the wildest disorder, they fled.

"Long live the Beggarmen!" cried the burghers of Leyden. And they opened their gates with shouts of joy, that the conquering fleet might sail up the canals and into the very city. Beneath the high-arched stone bridges, past rows of red brick houses, whose windows shone with welcome, the vessels glided along, whilst the Beggars threw loaves of bread to the crowds of famishing people. There, on the deck of his ship stood Tyl distributing food, and there too, stood Lammie, in his white cook's apron, throwing bread and herrings to the people. And he sighed for sympathy of their sorrow, and laughed for joy of their deliverance, and what with sighing and laughing, he found himself so anhungered, that he needs must exercise all his virtue not to consume a single crumb of the precious food himself.

Then at last Tyl and Lammie and the Admiral and the other Beggarmen went ashore. Joining the burghers, they marched down the street, all singing and shouting for gladness, to offer up thanks to God in the largest church in the city.

After that the ships of the Beggarmen sailed before the breeze through snows of winter and summer's heat. And Tyl and Lammie sailed with them. By sea, by river, they sailed until they had driven all King Philip's soldiers out of their land. Then the people cried:

"No longer will we have a King to rule us! Our country shall be a republic! Now the people shall make the laws! Now the people shall say who will rule them!"

And they chose their beloved hero, William of Orange, to be their chief governor. And when the Prince of Orange heard about all that Tyl had done to help drive out the Spaniards, he made Tyl the keeper of a tall, tall tower that stood beside the blue waters of the harbor in the town of Veere in Zeeland.

"Tyl, my friend," said the Prince, "you shall keep watch from that high tower over the harbor and the sea beyond."

"Aye, aye, sir!" Tyl answered. "I shall keep watch with the eyes of an eagle and the ears of an hawk to see that the King of Spain sends no more ships, no more soldiers to torment us!"

So Tyl went to live in the tower and he made Lammie his Chief Cook. Henceforth Lammie managed the boys who worked in the kitchen and he turned out the most wonderful, the most delicious things to eat. One day Tyl found him sitting in a fine chair before the fire on the kitchen hearth. He was shouting out orders to the boys, he was sending them scurrying every which way, to mind the meat on the spits, to stir up a gingerbread, a cake, to bring him the sauce for the goose that he might taste it and savor its flavor. Then Tyl gave Lammie such a slap on the shoulder he nearly sent the big fellow sprawling.

"Behold the great Lammie!" he laughed. "Lammie, the King of the Kitchen!" And he crowned Lammie with a string of onions and thrust a stalk of celery into his hand to serve as a kingly sceptre.

But Lammie jumped up in a twinkling. The crown of onions he threw on the floor. From the celery sceptre he took a bite and he started to chew it with a loud crunch of scorn for all kings.

"Nay, nay, Tyl!" he cried. "Neither in palaces nor in kitchens will we have Kings! So long as you and I both shall live, there shall be no King in the Netherlands!"

Tales of Tyl Ulenspiegel arose in Flanders, the Netherlands, and Germany in the fifteenth century. They are folk tales, woven about the name of a famous jester, who actually lived in Germany and wandered over Europe. Later versions of the stories in Belgium and Holland claimed Tyl as a Dutchman and placed him in the period of the struggle of the Netherlands for independence from Spain.

The Capture of Breda

A Tale from the Province of North Brabant

WHEN Philip the Spaniard found the United Provinces of the Netherlands snatched from his grasp, he issued a scandalous proclamation, offering honors and rewards to any ruffian who should serve his King, by murdering William of Orange. And there came a paltry wretch who stole into William's palace at Delft and shot the Father of his Country. Then all the Netherlands mourned, and who was there to champion the liberties of Holland against the power of Spain? Ah, it was well for Holland that the courage of Father William survived in his second son, Maurice, a boy of seventeen. With the help of that staunch old patriot, John van Olden Barneveldt, the lad was made Stadtholder of Holland and Zeeland, and for forty years to come,

This picture was suggested by a painting called *The Capture of Breda*, by the Spanish artist, Velasquez.

144

he was to uphold, in foul times and fair, the liberties of his land.

But in those troublous times, the southern provinces fell away from those at the north. Their hearts went out to Spain. They still wished to call her mother; and so they became the Spanish Netherlands, while the United Provinces of the North, in opposite wise, sought to drive the Spaniard out from every corner of their land. Thenceforth, through the ages, that line of division was to remain. The Spanish Netherlands grew into Belgium, the United Provinces into Holland.

And what, in those days, of the merry Duchy of Brabant, that spread out her fresh green fields along the river Maas and far to the southern borderland? Brabant, likewise, was split in two; her southern half fell to the Spanish Netherlands, her northern half to Holland. And Breda, the fortress with the towering castle, the trim and beautiful city, than which no fairer was to be found in all of merry Brabant,—what of Breda? Breda had belonged to William of Orange, but the Duke of Alva had taken the city, and still it lay languishing in the oppressive power of Spain. A Spanish garrison swaggered about its streets, the flag of Spain flew from its castle towers. In the great cathedral, the figures of Count Engelbert of Nassau and his lady carved of alabaster, lay side by side beneath a black marble canopy borne by four alabaster warriors; and from their tomb, that was the jewel of Breda, the two looked out in sadness. Once they had been the beloved lord and lady of that fair city, and now it was lost to William, the greatest of their race, lost to their house of Orange-Nassau, grievously ground down beneath the heel of Spain.

Then the youthful Stadtholder, Maurice, began to display his bril-

This picture was taken from an old Dutch print called "The Capture of Breda"

145

liant talents as a general. Both to weaken the power of the enemy and to recover his priceless possession, he determined to take Breda. But since he lacked sufficient troops for such a large undertaking, he made up his mind to capture the city by an exercise of his wits.

Now the fuel that was used in those days on the open hearths beneath the broad chimneys of Brabant, was either peat or wood. Peat was dried turf, cut in squares, and it came at that time, as it does today, from the heaths of Friesland, Drente, Overyssel, Groningen and Holland. Most of the skippers whose boats bore the peat to North Brabant, lived in the town of Leur, not far from Breda, and among these were two named van Bergen, who held a pass from the Spanish government granting them safe-conduct to carry their peat anywhere in Brabant. But Adrian van Bergen took it into his head to use his pass for the sore defeat of the Spaniards. Seeking out Prince Maurice, he said:

"Noble Sir, I go regularly with my boat into the fortress of Breda. In the lower part of the ship beneath a cargo of peat, you can hide some seventy soldiers whom I can thus carry in safety inside the walls of the castle. Once within the fortress, they will know very well what to do."

"The idea is good," said the Prince, and in March of the year 1590, he summoned Adrian to him and bade him go forward with his plan. Thus the boat was laden,—seventy soldiers in her hull, commanded by the nobleman, Charles de Herauiere, and above, a huge pile of peat. With this strange cargo, the skipper Adrian set forth on his adventure.

The journey went none too quickly, for ice and wind were against the Dutchmen. Moreover, as she struggled forward, the gallant boat sprang a leak. Down in the open space in her hull the sturdy soldiers sat crouched, knee deep in the icy water. But all such things have an end, and at length in the darkness of the night, they passed the frozen meadows and entered the city of Breda.

Then the Spaniards, dimly beholding the vessel, gliding ghostly in the shadows, said to themselves. "How glad we are to see a boat-load of peat. Peat makes a merry fire and the weather is cold. Aye, indeed! We welcome the thought of a fire."

But in that moment of crisis, what should occur? The bitterness of the cold, set some among the Dutchmen to a sudden coughing and sneezing. What would the Spaniards say if they heard a loud Kerchoo? Could turfs sneeze? Could peats cough? Nay, the Spaniards would know that their foes lay hidden on the barge, and would seize them and make an end of their plan to deliver the fortress.

And now the enemy they must fight, those soldiers in the boat, was a legion of coughs and sneezes. The warriors met them boldly. Stop!

Stay! Run! We refuse to cough or to sneeze. It was a gallant battle. And sixty-nine of these valiant warriors gained a glorious victory and were able to keep silent, but one among them, alack, unhappy Lieutenant Hels, could not master the coughing. The bigger the danger appeared, the more anxious he became, the more he coughed and sneezed.

At length the good fellow begged his comrades to make an end of his life, that he might not betray them all and defeat their enterprise; but Adrian, the boatman, had another plan to cover the tell-tale coughing. He began to pole more vigorously, with a mighty swishing and splashing and lapping of the water. Thus the noise of his poling quite covered up Lieutenant Hels's kerchoos.

Straight up to the grim gray walls of the castle, Adrian poled his barge, but there the challenge of a corporal rang out upon the night.

"Who goes there?"

"Adrian van Bergen with a boat-load of peat."

Well and good! The night was so cold that the Spanish soldiers were stamping their feet to keep warm. They did not waste any time in a further examination, but took hold of the ropes, and themselves drew the peat-barge inside the walls of the castle. Then Lieutenant Hels had to bury his face in his knees to keep from bursting forth on the night with a thunderous kerchoo!

On the following day the Spaniards unloaded the peat, while the Dutchmen beneath fairly held their breath. But toward nightfall Adrian told the workmen to wait for the daylight before they proceeded to finish their task.

"For," said he. "The rest must be carefully carried out. The best peat lies beneath."

During the night, this "best peat" crept out of the ship, overpowered the astonished garrison of the castle and opened the gates to Prince Maurice, who had been in hiding with his army in the neighborhood of the city.

Thus the city of Breda was returned to the house of Orange-Nassau, and the province of North Brabant saved for the United Provinces that formed the Dutch republic. Captain Heranguiere, for his bravery, was made the governor of the city. Adrian was given a generous pension, and to this very day a statue of him may be seen in the town of Leur, while the boat, the faithful peat-barge, was taken from the water and exalted into an honored position, where it might be preserved in the castle. For many a day thereafter, it was pointed out to all comers as the famous vessel, wherein the saviors of Breda had been conveyed to the fortress.

IN THE HAGUE THERE LIVES A COUNT
In Den Haag Daar Woont Een Graaf
In the Hague there lives a count,
And his son is Johnny;
If you ask, "Where lives your pa?"
With his hand points sonny.
First with his finger,
Then with his thumb,
In his hat he wears a plume;
Don't you think him bonny?
How d'y do, dear Johnny!

The Escape of Hugo de Groot

IN DAYS when Prince Maurice of Orange, son of William the Silent, was Stadtholder of Holland, and the Spaniards had been all but driven out of the land, there arose a fearful wrangling and squabbling between religious parties in the Dutch republic. And one party said: "Every man in Holland must believe what I believe!" And the other party said: "Nay, not so! Every man in Holland must believe what I believe!" And with that, they fell to fighting, hurling volleys of words at each other, and flinging self-will and hatred abroad, just as though neither side had ever heard that the Christian religion was founded on the simple law of love.

Well, at this time, there were certain men who had the wisdom to see that each man must believe what to him seems right, and that, if he be honest, he cannot be changed by force. And among these peace-loving gentlemen, were John van Olden Barneveldt, an old man, grown gray in devoted service to Prince Maurice, and one, Hugo de Groot, or Grotius, a young man of thirty-six, statesman, historian, poet, learned above all others in matters of the law.

And John van Olden Barneveldt and Hugo de Groot became leaders of the party that stood for patience and toleration, but Prince Maurice had opened his heart to jealousy of the fine old man to whom he owed so much. In whatever way he could he meant to stand against him, and so he became the leader of the opposing party, which would have forced its dogmas down every Dutchman's throat!

Then the States of Holland sent Grotius to Utrecht on business to the Party of Toleration which was powerful in that city. But Prince Maurice entered the town with troops. In anger and fear, he bade his soldiers disarm the civic guard, and he would have taken Hugo a prisoner, had he not fled for his life.

And now Prince Maurice had entered on a course from which he would not draw back. He was afraid of John van Olden Barneveldt. He was jealous of his power and the place he held in the hearts of the people; and so he had Grotius and the grand old man arrested and brought to trial. Olden Barneveldt was condemned to death, a hideous mistake which left on the name of Prince Maurice a stain he could never blot out. As to Grotius, he was condemned to life imprisonment in the fortress of Loewestein.

On a beautiful day in June of the year 1619, he was carried off to that lonely place, an island stronghold near the town of Gorcum, its grim old towers surrounded by water on every side. And Grotius was only thirty-six. What a young man he was to have naught to look forward to, save imprisonment all his days. From his little cell in the height of the tower, he could look out over all the broad land and breathe the free breezes that came and went, but he himself could not come and go. He was shut in there for life.

It was good that he was a scholar and could find a world for himself in books. He loved to read and to write, and a friend was allowed to send him books, which were returned at stated intervals in the great chest that bore his washing to Gorcum.

Now the wife of Hugo de Groot, one Maria van Reygersberg, was worthy of her husband, a woman of tender devotion, but likewise of spirit and courage. When friends asked why she did not throw herself at the feet of Prince Maurice and beg him to release her husband, she cried: "No, I will not do that. If Hugo has deserved this, let them strike off his head!" But though she would not beg where so much injustice had been shown, she did consent to ask the authorities for permission to share her husband's confinement. This favor was granted on one condition, that she should never come back if once she left the fortress. Accordingly one fine day, Maria arrived with Elsie, her maid, at Loewestein. Then the little gray cell was enlivened with the swishing of skirts, and the bright eyes and gentle laughter of women. But, better than that, Vrouw Maria and Elsie had come to use their wits. They looked down at the water around them and the guard of soldiers below and wondered how they could help Hugo to escape.

Soon Vrouw Maria noticed that the guard which had been exceedingly strict at first in searching Hugo's laundry chest whenever it went off to Gorcum, had grown quite careless of late. It had been so long a time that they had found nothing in it save harmless linen and books. On perceiving this, an idea struck Vrouw Maria,—her husband could be hidden in that chest and carried out in safety! She and Elsie whispered much together before they revealed the plan to de Groot.

Hugo smiled at the scheme, but he did as the women requested. Every day he lay in the chest with the top fastened down. A few air holes were made, and soon he had accustomed himself to staying in the stuffy little hole for a long time at a stretch. Then all was ready for action.

Great was the excitement of Lady Maria and her maid, when the great day came and two soldiers arrived for the chest. De Groot, they were told, was in bed, and the covers of his rude prison pallet were stuffed out in such a way that a figure appeared, indeed, to be lying beneath them. Elsie went along with the box to see that it was not roughly handled.

"Be careful," she said. "Don't you know that the books in that chest are of value. Nothing must happen to them."

"The chest's as heavy as though a man were hidden inside," one of the soldiers grumbled,—a moment of awful suspense for de Groot, but Maria, his wife, calmly answered:

"Books are heavy things."

Then the chest vanished out of the cell and was carried off on a canal boat. Thus it arrived at last at the home of Hugo's friend. Scarcely had the prisoner stepped safely from his painful hiding place, when he was helped to dress in the costume of a mason. Bending his head beneath the weight of a hod, he made his way to Paris.

And all this time, Vrouw Maria had bravely remained behind in the cell, in order that none might suspect what great thing was going forward. Not until she was certain that Hugo was out of the land, did she inform the guard what had happened. Then, you may well believe, a great hue and cry was raised, but raised in vain. Hugo was safe on his way. The angry authorities suggested that Maria should be retained in her husband's stead, but public opinion ran too high. All Holland applauded what she had done, and so they were forced to set her free.

Thenceforward Grotius lived in Paris, Sweden, England or Germany, with Maria and his children, but he never again came back for any long stay in Holland. In the pretty chateau of a kindly French nobleman, he wrote the book of which his countrymen are most proud, *Concerning the law of War and Peace,* the first great book that ever set down the laws which should govern nations in their relations to each other. Before de Groot no such international law had ever been worked out. It was the first step in getting nations to work together and consider each other's rights. And for this reason, above all others, Holland is proud of Hugo de Groot, whom the world has called the Father of International Law.

Great Days in Holland

The King of Smiles, Franz Hals (1580-1666)

IN HAARLEM, on the street called Peeuselaersteeg, lived one Franz Hals, a painter of portraits, with his wife, Lysbeth. They were a jolly couple. They laughed in the morning; they laughed at noon; they laughed at night. Indeed, they loved nothing better than laughter.

On fine afternoons Franz put on his wide-brimmed black beaver hat and went for a stroll about Haarlem, passing the time of day in genial fashion with the burghers of his acquaintance. Along the banks of the Spaarne with its jumble of boats, he wandered, through the great square with the old town hall, and past the tall mass of the Groote Kerk. Ah, the Dutch in those days were a proud and happy folk. They walked with a swagger, in their silks and ruffs and fine laces. They had fought the long fight for freedom and won. They had "singed the beard of the King of Spain," and driven the Spaniard out of their land. Their vessels sailed the Seven Seas, their sturdy adventurers roamed afar, discovering

152

lands before unknown. And, to crown their glory, a series of brilliant painters had suddenly appeared, to startle the world with the beauty of their pictures.

As Franz walked the streets of Haarlem, he greeted many a fellow member of the Civic Guard, or dropped into some stately old Guild Hall where the guardsmen met, as in little clubs, to hold shooting contests or banquets. And it chanced that the officers of the Guild of St. Joris began to say:

"It is long enough that we have seen kings and dukes and counts looking down at us from the portraits on our Guild-house walls. Let us put the kings and the dukes in the cellar and have our own faces painted to hang in the places of honor."

So the officers sent for Franz Hals at the time of their yearly banquet. He came to the Guild Hall as they sat around the table with the last of their food still before them. There they were, twelve in number, with ruffs about their necks, all dressed in dark-colored clothes relieved by scarlet silk sashes. Middle-aged men they were, full-bearded and moustachioed, save for the two dandy standard-bearers who were little more than youths. And the Colonel, Pieter Schoutts Jacobsen, a stout old fellow, who was sitting with his back to Franz, turned around, with his right arm akimbo, and quoth with a genial smile:

"We would have you paint our portraits, Franz Hals, to hang on the Guild-house walls."

Then Franz set to work in good earnest and painted the officers just as he had seen them, bold and laughing around the table, a genial, masterful group. And no sooner had the good folk of Haarlem beheld the finished picture, with its figures all so lifelike, than the officers of all the other shooting guilds in Haarlem wished to follow suit, and have pictures painted, likewise. Soon an endless procession of sitters began to besiege Franz's studio, demanding to have their portraits. And Herman and Sara and Jan and Franz and the rest of the little Halses, peeping through the curtain of their father's sanctum, saw a wondrous array of full-dress mynheers and mevrouws sitting before his easel. There was Mevrouw van Beresteyn in a velvet brocade with a gold embroidered stomacher sticking out stiffly a mile in front of her. There was Mynheer van Huythuysen, with an excellently good conceit of himself, his left arm on his hip, his right arm extended to rest his magnificent sword on the ground, and his head, in its wide beaver hat, held high in the air as one who would say: "And what do you think of me? That's what I'd like to know!"

Often it happened, too, that the full-dress mynheers and mevrouws brought with them to Franz's studio exceedingly full-dress children, who wriggled and squirmed in their satins and laces, and would far rather have played than have had the honor of being painted. Indeed, they could not be kept out of mischief, but played all sorts of high jinks, in spite of their costly finery, and made monkey faces at any small Hals, whose bright eyes might chance to appear through the opening of the curtains.

Ah! those were happy days, days when the little Halses had plenty of money to spend on heete koeken and sweetmeats, for these burghers paid Franz good guilders, a generous price for their pictures.

One day Vrouw Hals, the jolly Lysbeth, said to her goodman, Franz:

"Franz, you are getting famous painting other husbands and wives! Why don't you paint yourself and me, pray tell?"

And she put on her best Sunday-go-to-meeting dress of black brocade with its stylish purple bodice, and went to the expense of the newest things in ruffs and cuffs and caps. Then she made Franz don his town hall suit of black silk and brocade, his best beaver hat, his cambric cuffs, and his collar of fine Mechlin lace. Sitting down beside him on a bench, she put her hand on his shoulder and said:

"Now, Franz, paint us like this!"

But as she sat there, desiring to look impressive like a sober and dignified matron, Franz told her a funny story, a story so funny that she could not keep her face straight. She laughed and laughed and laughed. And

Franz, the rascal, painted her just like that, trying to straighten her face that was a-tremble with laughter.

And there in that picture on the walls of the Ryks Museum in Amsterdam, they sit to this very day, all in a garden green beneath a shady tree, with a sunny vision of fountains and marble pavilions beyond.

But Franz, for all his success, began to come in for a great deal of trouble in painting his huge group pictures of the officers of the guilds. Captain Visscher would come with his lordliest swagger, to interrupt the artist's work and say that Captain Van der Venne was standing in front of him and shutting him out of the picture, and since he was paying the same amount as his friend for the honor of having his portrait painted, he must demand that his own figure be brought forward where it could be seen to the best advantage; or Captain de Herbst would drop in to twirl his moustache and say that he noticed he was being painted so that only three quarters of his face was turned to the front and he must really insist most positively on having his full face shown! Such bickerings and corrections! There must be naught but a row of figures, all equally large, all turned full face to the front! What a problem for an artist, whose artist's soul demanded that some figures be in the background and some in the front, with a variety of positions. At last Franz settled the question once for all. He would paint no more portraits in rows, but,—and here he showed his cleverness—those who paid the most should have the places of honor! Henceforth the Colonel, who was generally one of the wealthiest members of the guild, had to bid up and pay a very high fee to become the most conspicuous figure; captains paid for second place, lieutenants for third, while sergeants must needs be content with peeping out from the rear.

It was a troublesome business at best, painting these worthy burghers. What Franz really loved was laughter. He liked to wander away from the respectable patrons of his studio to the bustling fish-market in search of more picturesque subjects—fishwives crying their wares, queer old sailor-men, tavern heroes with mug or flute or viol, saucy young market lassies boldly passing him by with a quick-flung joke or a jibe. He joined the rollicking company at kermisses and fairs in the country round about. He played high jinks with every one who would laugh, and a series of jovial couples and merry groups danced off his palette, the merriest of figures. Their mouths laugh; their eyes laugh; their noses laugh; their cheeks laugh. What do they care for, but pranks and frolics?

Down by the sea among the sand-dunes, which rise high as little hills along the coast near Haarlem, Franz met fisher lads and lassies, strong

Mevrouw van Beresteyn

and blithe of build, full of life's gaiety. Scores of these he painted.

Indeed, he painted so many dirty urchins and beggar children, that people began to twit him with the lack of a sense of elegance. To prove that he had not entirely lost his love for what was fine, he painted the infant son of a wealthy tulip-grower of Haarlem, an elegant little rascal, in the arms of his good-natured nurse. The dress of the child is a splendid piece of gold brocade, with the lace so carefully painted it seems as though Franz must have cut off a length of rare Mechlin point and pasted it on the canvas. But in spite of his finery, the tiny imp has a mischievous smile, as he seizes the brooch at his nurse's neck.

Now at this time, Franz had living with him, besides his own lively children, several young lads who were learning to paint. Among these apprentices, were that monkey, Adrian Brouwer, and the brothers, Adrian and Isaac van Ostade. Adrian van Ostade painted peasants merry-making, and Isaac painted winter scenes, frozen canals with skaters and sledges on the ice. These rascals loved laughter as well as Franz. Sometimes they painted on the sidewalk bits of money, tempting pieces of gold or silver. Then they hid themselves to watch how passers would try to pick up the treasure. So carefully had they done their painting, so true in each detail, that scarcely a man or woman came by, who did not stoop down and try in vain to pick up the painted coins.

Franz Hals' picture of his pupil, Adrian Brouwer,
as The Fool.

Between the years 1630 and 1640, Franz was recognized as the foremost painter of Holland. To Haarlem, as to an artists' Mecca, flocked teachers and students from every land. Now in those days, Frederick Henry of Nassau, Prince of Orange, and son of William the Silent, had succeeded his older brother, Maurice, as Stadtholder of the Netherlands. Under Frederick Henry, the Dutch finally defeated the Spaniards and drove them from every corner of their land. At such a pitch of power and glory, Frederick Henry summoned Anthony Van Dyck of Antwerp, a Flemish artist, to Holland, to paint a family portrait.

Mynheer van Huythuysen

Van Dyck, who had studied under the great Flemish master, Rubens, had been for the past ten years court painter to James I of England. Having finished his work for the Stadtholder, and being on the point of embarking again for England, Van Dyck wished to see for himself Franz Hals, the master about whom gossip had spun such wonderful stories.

One bright morning in June 1630, Van Dyck knocked at Franz's front door. Vrouw Hals greeted the stranger politely, though he did not tell her his name.

"My husband is not at home," she said, but she sent her son, Jan, to look for his father. Jan found Franz in the little back room of a tavern.

"There's a smart gentleman all the way from The Hague to see you," said the lad. "And he wants you to paint his portrait."

Franz Hals

Franz left his retreat in bad humor. "It's the dickens of a nuisance to be interrupted," he scolded. And he welcomed the stranger coolly.

But Van Dyck, never telling his name, offered him a tempting fee if he would paint his portrait. Picking up an old canvas from the floor, Franz began to lay on the paint, with unwilling but masterly hand, and in a couple of hours he had completed such a likeness that his visitor was delighted.

"Now," said Van Dyck, "I beg one more favor. Let me, in return, paint you."

Franz opened his eyes in amazement, but he seated himself in the model's chair, and, as the stranger progressed in his work, he grew more and more astounded.

"Why?" he cried. "There is but one man in the world who could paint such a portrait! You must be Anthony Van Dyck!"

Now Van Dyck had been summoned to England by Charles I, to paint himself and his court, and he eagerly urged Franz to go with him across the channel. But no inducements whatever could move Franz out of Holland. Holland was his world. Dutch of the Dutch was Franz.

So Van Dyck sailed off for England alone, and Franz went back to his pots. Year after year passed by, till the pots became too much for him. Love of laughter and junketing, companioning with tavern heroes made a drunkard of Franz. He began to grow lazy and shiftless. No fine procession of mynheers and mevrouws came now to his studio. He painted little, and poverty began to look in at the windows of the house on Peeuselaersteeg. There were no extra pennies for heete koeken and goodies. But Lysbeth did not chide him. Whatever her good man did, she never scolded. Her love was warm and tender. In spite of his faults, they still continued to smile and laugh together.

At seventy, Franz delighted, as he had in earlier years, to wander off to the market, but his friends were no longer lads and lassies. He hobnobbed now with a few ancient cronies. One old lady in particular took his fancy. She was ugly as a scarecrow, but the striking play of her features and the wrinkles of her leathery skin fascinated Franz. Men called her Hille Bobbe, and she lived in a hovel by the Fish-market. She used her tongue and let every man know what she thought of him and his, if he happened to displease her. Franz painted her once, holding a tankard, with an owl perched on her shoulder, and her mouth open as though she were screeching shrilly her opinion of some interloper.

And now the colors on Franz's palette grew dark and dull and gray. His pictures were full of shadows and so was his life. Poorer and poorer he grew. Shabbier and shabbier grew the house on Peeuselaersteeg. One after another, his good bits of furniture had to be sold. The place looked sadly down at heels, pathetic, ragged and seedy.

Then certain old chums of Franz, who were on the Board of the Old Woman's Alms House in Haarlem, met in solemn conclave and agreed to commission the aged master to paint two portrait groups—one of themselves and one of the Lady Governors of the Old Woman's Home. At the age of eighty-four, Franz painted these two groups. They were not distinguished for youth or beauty, or swaggering with conscious power like his early soldier groups, but the old ladies, in particular, were attractive in their sternness, their garments as plain as their persons, but their faces alight with interest, eager, intelligent, bright.

And so the last days of Franz, thanks to his loyal friends, were busy and happy, with work well repaid, and Lysbeth, his life-long comrade, still smiling by his side.

Jan Steen, the Laughing Philosopher (1626-1679)

NOW when the brush fell from the hands of old Franz, the King of Smiles, who was to carry on the smile in painting? Well, there was Franz's student, Adrian Van Ostade, who painted merrymakings and junketings of peasants with no less joy than Franz, and there was Adrian Van Ostade's student, Jan Steen of Leyden, who had often made merry with Franz. Jan to be sure, was no less jolly a fellow than Franz.

Jan's father, who was a brewer, did not think much of painting as a means of earning a living. "No," said he. "There's nothing in painting. I'll set my son up as a brewer." And he was as good as his word. But Jan and his good wife, Greet, were a happy-go-lucky pair. They had little eye for business. When times were dull and customers few, Greet said to Jan with a shake of her head:

"If you are to pay the landlord, there must be more life in this place."

Jan said he would see to that, and off he went to the market. But did he bring home customers? No, he brought home geese. These he put in the kettle ordinarily used for brewing, where they flapped their wings in excitement and flew noisily about with a mighty stir and racket.

Greet came running into the room. What on earth was the matter!

"Well," said Jan. "You said there must be more life in this place. Is there now enough life to suit you?"

Then Greet fell a-laughing and Jan fell a-laughing, but the landlord who came to collect his rent could by no means see the joke. What was to be done, indeed, with such a clownish couple?

Often Jan had to pay off his debts with pictures instead of money. Ten or twenty guilders apiece contented him for a picture. He had a good heart, did Jan, but no head for business whatever. Nevertheless, if a customer beat him down, and drove too hard a bargain, he rewarded the miserly skinflint with a joke at his expense. Once a man insisted on having a picture of Noah's Flood for a price that would scarcely have purchased a string of first-class sausages. Jan agreed, but he did not intend to spend his time painting a lot of objects for such a price as that. When the picture was completed, it consisted of nothing but a sheet of water, in the midst of which floated a large Dutch cheese bearing the coat-of-arms of Leyden. The astonished purchaser cried out in dismay. How was this a picture of Noah's Flood, and what was the meaning of that cheese with the coat-of-arms?

"Why, the cheese proves," said Jan, "that there were Dutchmen on the earth before the flood."

"But where are Noah and the Ark?" cried the purchaser.

"O," replied Jan. "They are just beyond the point I painted in the picture!"

But for all his roistering and recklessness, Jan was a lovable fellow. He painted the comedy of human life with genial toleration—tavern scenes of jollity, card parties, marriage feasts, festivals of St. Nicholas, and children. Ah! what children!

Once on St. Nicholas Day, Jan Steen's whole family gathered together, to enjoy the gifts St. Nicholas had left the night before in the shoes of the children. One little girl went toddling about with a pail full of toys and a doll clasped tight in her arms. Tenderly the mother held out her arms toward the happy child. Behind these two, a big boy with a baby perched on his arm, pointed skyward to show the baby and a little fellow beside him how St. Nicholas came riding over the roofs on his great white horse and listened at the chimneys to find out if they had been good. Beside this group, a little boy, his eyes dancing with mischief, pointed laughingly to his big brother, who was howling in dire distress and digging one fist in his eyes. Alack, he had set out his shoe the night before, but what had he received? Nothing, nothing at all, nothing, that is, but a switch. He had been a naughty boy. St. Nicholas had brought

161

him nothing, nothing but a switch. His older sister joined the little fellow in laughing at the offender, while Grandfather Steen sat smiling in the center of the group. But, in the background stood Grandma, and what was Grandma doing? If no one else felt sorry for the lad who had been naughty, there was still Grandma. She was going out of the room, but as she went, she turned around and smiled and beckoned. Ah, Grandmothers' hearts are very soft! She could not let her grandson take his punishment unrelieved. She meant to beckon him out of the room and give him something in secret to make up for the switch in his shoe.

It was thus that Jan Steen set the family down to live through the ages on canvas. All across the front of the picture he painted a litter of things,—a child's shoe, two bright colored balls, a basket full of little cakes, each painted in such detail that one can see the squares in the waffles, and could almost pick off the nuts and the tiny black caraway seeds that adorn the crisp, brown cookies. Against a table leans a great square loaf of bread with chickens and animals traced on the crust, and how that crust shines with butter!

No picture could better express the sense of innocent family festivity. The room, indeed, is a muddle. The mother has hard work before her, if she would restore it to a Dutch pitch of order and cleanliness, but how jolly every one is. To this very day, when the dignified quiet of Dutch family life has been disturbed by feasting or upset by the play of children, with toys strewn all about, they say in Holland:

"This looks like a household by Jan Steen."

Merry old Jan Steen, the Laughing Philosopher of Dutch Art.

The King of Shadows, Rembrandt Van Ryn (1606-1669)

But what of the man who could not paint smiles, whose faces are often grave, or lit with eager intelligence, who set himself with zeal to master deeper human expressions,—Rembrandt van Ryn?

One day the miller who lived on the ramparts overlooking the Rhine in the pleasant city of Leyden, walked abroad with a beaming face. A son had arrived at his house, little Rembrandt van Ryn. Rembrandt had, from the first, an eye for the picturesque. As he grew to be a lad, he would stand, with his fancy all alive, watching the slow-moving barges gliding along the canals, the windmills never at rest, and the play of light and shadows over the flat green meadows. He liked to paint, but he cared not a straw for his other studies, and so one day his father placed him in the workshop of an artist. Beggars and every quaint figure he met, the boy put down in color, but most of all what was it he loved? He loved to study light and shade. A bonfire, with the figures nearest in vivid light, arresting instant attention, and all the rest of the world in dark mysterious shadow—that was a scene which delighted the boyish heart of Rembrandt.

By-and-by his work attracted attention. He went to Amsterdam, most elegant of Dutch cities, lordly Venice of the North, with her handsome shaded canals, and her brilliant flower market, and her stately burgher palaces built on myriad piles. And there came to him a stream of people wishing to sit for their portraits. Soon his workshop was a beehive, with scores of eager young pupils each busy in his own little cell, dressing up in the studio costumes to pose for one another, or studying the expressive faces of his dear old father and mother. And Gerard Dou and Nicholas Maes and others the world was to know were among his youthful pupils.

Then the handsome Rembrandt married a beautiful Frisian maiden, Saskia Van Ulenburgh, who brought him a little fortune. She was a daughter of the Burgomaster of Leeuwarden who was said to have dined with William the Silent on the very day he was shot by a murderer's hand in his princely palace at Delft.

Rembrandt loved Saskia dearly and she became at once the center of his life. He painted her portrait in a score of different ways, as women out of the Bible, as Bathseba or Samson's wife, or simply as herself. He dressed her up in silks and satins and pearls, and how proud he was of her hair, her long, flowing locks of gold. Nor did he neglect to paint himself, himself in jaunty fashion, with a feather in his hat. Ah, those were happy days! Florins he earned in plenty, but they went through his hands like a sieve. He spent them as fast as they came. For him they seemed to have wings.

Now the street on which Rembrandt lived was in the Jewish quarter. It swarmed with Dutch and Portuguese Jews in turbans and picturesque clothes of vivid and varied colors. Many a Jewish rabbi sat for him, as a model, and he painted the figures in his great Bible pictures wearing just the clothes which he saw on the Jews of his day, as he studied them from his window.

His home was a show place in Amsterdam. If a stranger wished to see something fine, he must visit the house of Rembrandt. There were pictures and antiques, coins and porcelains, ivories, bronzes, native East Indian dresses, weapons and musical instruments, a colorful mixture of objects of art, brought from all the ends of the earth; for those were the days when Dutch fleets were sailing all over the world, laying the foundation of Holland's great colonial empire, to New Amsterdam in America, to Java, Japan, and China, whence they brought home an endless array of rare and beautiful things.

The Night Watch by Rembrandt

Aye, those were great days for Amsterdam, days when she shone because of her painters, her merchants and her sailors, and, likewise, because of her poets. On the broad steps that led from the house of Jan Six, truest and sincerest of Rembrandt's friends and patrons, was often to be seen Joost van den Vondel, a stocking merchant by trade, but, by right of genius, the greatest of all Dutch poets. Over at the home of the poet, Roemer Visscher, which was graced by the presence of his two lovely daughters, Anna and Tesselschade, there gathered a group of notable guests,—Vondel, and Hooft, and their friend, Sir Constantyn Huygens, Secretary to the Stadtholder, Frederick Henry. In Roemer Visscher's garden, with Anna and Tesselschade, Vondel forgot his stockings and told his two pretty listeners of Saartje, his little daughter, who raced and played by Amsterdam's still canals, beneath the quiet trees.

164

My little Saartje, lively, gay and good,
  Was the joy of the neighborhood:
Ah, how she skipped the jump-rope with light feet,
  Or sang a song so sweet;
  Or with the others came,
  Circling in a game,
Or, followed by a merry, noisy troop,
  Drove the jingling hoop;
Or in the swing, with gayest laughter, swayed,
  Or with her dollie played;
  Foreshadowing later joys,
  That take the place of toys;
Or with jackstone and ball, must needs obey
  The childhood law of play,
And tossed and caught the dancing ivory round,
  Picked up the jackstones from the ground;
  Nor would have given these pleasures
  In exchange for treasures.

And when Vondel had finished entertaining the ladies with his graceful, beautiful lines, Huygens, that clever fellow, was there to set them laughing with some witty verse of this sort:

I saw thieves leave my house with sacks and packs last night;
I followed and addressed them in manner most polite.
I said: "Good sirs, beg pardon! My boldness pray forgive;
But since you're so kind as to move me, please show me where
     I'm to live!"

It was Huygens who saw to it that the Stadtholder, Frederick Henry, paid his bills to Rembrandt if he now and then ordered a picture.

In 1642 Rembrandt's pleasant years came to an end. His beloved Saskia died, leaving a little son, Titus. Then Rembrandt's light seemed to go out. He grew moody and stern and sad. In that very same year he painted a huge picture called *The Night Watch, or the Sortie of the Banning Cock Company of Civic Guards.* There were twenty-nine life-size figures, issuing pell-mell from a club house, all animation and bustle. You can almost hear the beat of the drums, the barking of the dog. The strong light picks out the figure of a lieutenant in a citron-yellow uniform with a blue sash, the captain in black velvet with a scarlet sash, a musketeer in red, and a little girl in yellow. The others are in shade, the deep shade that Rembrandt so loved to paint.

This picture, one of the greatest that was ever to come from Rembrandt's ready brush, succeeded in his time, only in arousing against him a storm of indignation. He had got himself into trouble at last with his love of light and shade.

"Why should the fellow put me in the shadows where no one can see me?" indignantly cried one and then another of those worthy officers whose faces could scarcely be seen. "We all paid the same to be painted, —save that little girl who paid not a penny. And he has dared to put her in the light in the center of the picture!"

But Rembrandt cared all too little. He was an independent fellow. He painted as he liked, and Saskia was no longer here,—he did not care, as he had before, for either praise or money. If the world did not like his paintings, so much the worse for the world. He went his own way, and painted as he chose, a giant of a fellow, with strength in every line.

But the world began to forget him and turn to more popular painters. Day by day, he lost favor, his income fell away. Soon he grew so poor that he had to sell his beautiful house. He was stripped of everything he possessed. There did not even remain to him a bit of table linen. And few of his friends stood by him, save the honest Jan Six, who helped and employed him through all his dark days of trouble.

In spite of appearances, nevertheless, no real failure was here, for Rembrandt worked quietly on amid the ruin of his affairs, calmly conceiving and painting still more beautiful pictures. And today men speak of him lovingly as the greatest painter of Holland.

Gerard Dou, the Little Master (1613-1675)

In days when Rembrandt's pictures sold for a song, there was one among his students who could get a thousand florins for a tiny two foot canvas. This was Gerard Dou of Leyden. Nobody cared for a Rembrandt, but a Dou was a royal gift. When King Charles II returned from Holland to England, the States General of the Dutch republic presented him with a painting by Dou as the choicest of their art treasures.

So tiny were the pictures of Dou, and so carefully painted every detail, that one must look through a magnifying glass to take in all their wonders. A fussy, particular man was Dou. He would work for days on a hand, one day on each finger. None ever surpassed him in painting cabbages, and ah, how he could paint broomsticks! One could actually count the twigs of which the broomstick was made! One day a friend paid him a compliment on a broomstick in a picture. But Dou replied, "I have still three days' work to do before I complete that broomstick!"

It was little, indeed, that Dou learned from Rembrandt, his great master. He had none of Rembrandt's rugged strength. From him he took nothing more than his charm of light and shade. His tiny *Night School* in the candlelight, with its contrast of light and shadow, is a pocket edition of Rembrandt's huge and splendid *Night Watch*. The genius of Gerard Dou was not the genius of power. It was the genius of patience, of taking infinite pains.

Vermeer of Delft, rejoicing in cool, clear blues and quiet, elegant figures, and Peter de Hooch, with his charming views through open doors, were friends of Gerard Dou's, all little masters, who painted on tiny canvases, simple domestic scenes, genuine, radiant, sweet.

And the end of the story is this—no country has ever given the world, in a single age, such a group of great painters as Holland. French paintings were made for palaces, Italian paintings for churches, but Dutch pictures were made for homes, for homes or guild-halls of burghers, to be lived with, day by day, in intimate, tender friendship.

Lazy-Goody Land

Luilekkerland

Merrily children come in crowds
    Crawling through mountains of rice;
Ho, for Lazy-goody Land,
    And everything that's nice!
Are streets there paved with brick? Why no!
    With pastry, cake and pie;
And if you wish, just help yourself,
    As you are passing by.

The houses in this wonderland
    Are made of fudge so sweet;
The gardens fenced with sausages,
    Along the public street.
And pancakes, like balloons, they say,
    Are floating in the air;
The rivers flow with foaming milk,
    And trees bear cookies there.

What will you drink now,—chocolate?
 The founts with choc'late flow;
Or if it's pop you'd rather have,
 To yonder Pop Pond go.
The snow is powdered sugar white,
 With syrup-honey rain;
The hail is almonds, raisins, prunes,
 O, let's go there again!

MYNHEER DE WITT

Under the bridge there lies a mouse,
Pray is Mr. de Witt in the house?
No Mynheer has gone away,
Guess now whom he met today.
Ten iron men,
Ten pots and pans,
Ten children without a soul;
They hopped, they skipped, they ran,
Bread and butter and bran!
Bread and butter and sauce,
You're the boss!

The Black Tulip

Told from the novel by Alexander Dumas

IN HAARLEM, in the year 1672, men's minds were filled with but a single thought,—tulips, tulips, tulips. There were acres of beautiful fields about the town aflame in Springtime with the vivid fire of the blossoms. Aye, if the truth were told, the good burghers had lost their heads over tulips. They would pay as high as a thousand florins for a single fancy bulb. Holland might be at war with England, France, or Spain,—what cared the tulip growers of Haarlem? They could not be bothered to think of so ugly a thing as war, when all their thoughts were full of their lovely, innocent blossoms.

And it was not in Haarlem alone, that men had gone mad over tulips. In the quaint old town of Dort, crowning with its ancient gables the meeting point of the Maas with three other stately rivers, lived one Cornelius van Baerle, a student and an artist. Cornelius had studied painting in the elegant studio of Gerard Dou. He loved beauty, he loved quiet. But he cared not at all for battles, for musketry and cannon.

In his boyhood, when the ships of the Dutch East India Company were swarming over all the seas, laying the foundation of Holland's great colonial empire, English and Dutch had flown at each other's throats to gain the mastery of the ocean. Then that doughty old warrior, Admiral Tromp, of whom Holland was so proud, had defeated the English fleet in a series of naval battles, and sailed the English Channel with a broom defiantly fastened to the top of his tallest mast, thus signifying to all the world that he had swept the seas clean of the English. But, in spite of all the hurrahs, Cornelius had not been stirred. He had no passion for war. The broom of Admiral Tromp aroused no thrill within his breast.

Years later, his godfather, Cornelius de Witt, himself a naval officer, took the youth aboard "The Seven Provinces," Admiral de Ruyter's flagship at the battle of Southwold Bay. Cornelius looked on unafraid during all the cannonading, but after he had witnessed twenty ships blown to pieces, 3,000 men killed, and 5,000 wounded, he had innocently enquired:

"And who has won the victory, the English or the Dutch?"

To which de Ruyter replied, in manner quite unconcerned:

"Neither. The matter is undecided. We shall have to fight again."

"Well," thought Cornelius van Baerle, "if, after all this destruction, both sides claim the victory and neither is the least better off, war is a foolish matter." And he bade farewell to de Ruyter and his godfather, Cornelius de Witt, and retired to his home in Dort, a handsome red brick

house, all trim and tidy and neatly scoured behind its screen of poplars. And there he took it into his head to choose the most elegant and expensive fad of his time. In a word, he became a tulip fancier, and no sooner had he applied his keen intelligence and inexhaustible patience to the matter of growing tulips, than he succeeded better than anyone else at either Haarlem or Leyden in varying the colors, changing the shape and producing entirely new species. Soon from Dordrecht to Mons, men

172

talked of nothing but Mynheer van Baerle's tulips. His beds, pits, drying room, and drawers for keeping bulbs, were visited with awe by strangers in his city.

Now this was all very well, but, quite unbeknown to Cornelius, he had living directly next door, a secret and envious rival. Mynheer Isaac Boxtel had long been raising tulips. He had even produced one bulb which had come to the hands of the King of Portugal, who had condescended to say that the flower was really "not bad." Nevertheless, Myn-

heer Isaac had neither the wit nor the patience which made success for his wealthy neighbor. He could not work out the problem of producing such wonderful blossoms. And so when he saw a new wing for the drying and care of bulbs added to the house of Cornelius, and beheld in the beds of his garden the most beautiful new kinds of tulips, he began to grow green with envy. Behind a sycamore tree, trained against his own garden wall, he set up a ladder, and from the top of this secret perch, he spied on his neighbor's yard and saw all that came to pass! He even purchased a telescope, in order to miss no smallest detail of what went on in the home of Cornelius. And as he had the long instrument fixed to his eye, he would fancy that it was a musket, and he was taking aim at Cornelius. Then he would feel with his finger for the trigger and imagine that he was firing the shot which should strike his rival down.

When the Cornelius de Witt and three other of Van Baerle's new kinds of tulips were flowering in his garden, dazzling in their beauty, the miserable jealous wretch was so filled with rage, that he felt he must destroy them. One evening he tied two cats together by their hind legs and threw them over the wall into the midst of that princely garden. The terrified animals rushed across the bed each in a different direction. Then, finding themselves fast bound by the string, they tore back and forth among the flowers with hideous miauing. Not until after a furious strife, did they succeed in breaking loose from each other and vanish in the darkness.

The next morning when Van Baerle went to his garden, he percieved all at once that his symmetrical rows of tulips were in complete disorder, like the ranks of a battalion in the midst of which a shell has fallen. He ran to them in dismay, all the color leaving his cheeks. But, thanks be to God, though fifteen or twenty choice tulips were lying about, torn and crushed and withering, the Cornelius de Witt, and the three other tulips which Isaac had meant to destroy, had not been harmed at all. Proudly they raised their noble heads above the corpses of their slain companions. This was enough to comfort the simple soul of Van Baerle, and to make Isaac Boxtel tear his hair when he learned how he had been thwarted. Henceforth, Van Baerle bade one of the under-gardeners to sleep in a box near the flower-beds, and guard the precious blossoms.

Now about this time, the Tulip Society of Haarlem offered a prize of 100,000 florins for the production of a large black tulip without a spot of color, a feat which many florists believed was altogether impossible. Nevertheless, the thoughts of all the tulip-growing world were soon filled with naught but the great black tulip. Van Baerle was among those who thought the thing could be done and set to work to try, but Boxtel pooh-

poohed the whole matter. "You might as well set out to find a white blackbird," he said.

Patiently, Van Baerle began to change the color of his tulips. He changed them from red to brown, and from brown to dark brown, till by the following year, Boxtel beheld in his garden, flowers of so dark a color, that there was no room left for uncertainty,—by the very next Spring Van Baerle would have the coveted black. There was no doubt whatever about it. Then Isaac allowed his own bulbs to rot in the pits, and his tulips to wither in the beds, and he gave up trying himself, while he spent all his time spying through the telescope.

Since the new wing, built by his neighbor, was almost entirely of glass, it lay quite open to view with its cabinets and cupboards, and ticketed pigeonholes. No curtains were ever drawn, for Van Baerle was far too pure of heart to dream of a jealous rival. At night when the room was lit by a lamp, Isaac could see Van Baerle sorting his seeds and soaking them in liquids designed to deepen their colors; he saw him heat certain grains, then moisten and combine them by a sort of delicate grafting. This innocent magic, the fruit of childlike musings and manly genius combined, this patient, untiring labor of which Boxtel was quite incapable, inflamed a thousand-fold his hot, devouring envy.

One night he saw the windows of the drying room suddenly light up. Then two dark figures appeared. One was Van Baerle himself. The other, tall, stern, majestic, was his godfather, Cornelius de Witt, inspector of dykes and brother of John de Witt, Grand Pensionary of the Provinces. Isaac saw Cornelius de Witt give Van Baerle a package, which appeared to be of the utmost importance. He saw Van Baerle accept it and place it unopened, far back in one of his cabinets, behind the tulip bulbs.

"Ah," thought Isaac with ugly exultation. "Here is a secret, that I may one day turn to account and use against that fellow."

The truth of the matter was that the two de Witts in those days, were none too popular in Holland. Never did Holland have truer, more high-souled patriots, more cruelly misunderstood, than these two great brothers, de Witt.

Years before, the Stadtholder, Frederick Henry, had thought it would be a good thing to secure for his family the right of succeeding him as Stadtholder, Captain and Admiral General; so he got the States to pass a bill securing to his son, William II, the right of inheriting these offices. When William II passed away, the followers of the House of Orange desired to hail his infant son, the merest tiny baby, as the Stadtholder, William III. And they sang this song in the land:

Though our young prince is still so wee—
hurrah!
Yet shall he our Stadtholder be—
hurrah!
Though reeds may break and trees may bend
The House of Orange shall not end!
O, long live Orange, hurrah!
O, long live Orange, hurrah!

But such a passing on of power from father to son savored too much of kingship and too little of a republic, where he, who is to govern, is elected by the people. The two de Witts, John and Cornelius, strenuously opposed it. The Kings of Spain were tyrants. They could not imagine a kingdom where the people governed themselves, and they did not intend to permit their beloved Holland to suffer beneath the oppressive power of a Stadtholder turned into a King. So the baby William was set aside, and John got the States to pass a bill abolishing forever the dangerous office of Stadtholder, while he himself was chosen Grand Pensionary or President of Holland. For years he so guided affairs that, in spite of the wars with England, there was prosperity for Dutchmen abroad as well as at home.

But in those days, gross selfishness and fear governed nations in their relations to one another. Each was trying to clutch all it could, seeking

to increase its own power by alliances with others, and constantly threatening those neighbors with whom it had not made a league. And John
de Witt judged that it was in the best interests of Holland to make a
peaceful alliance with France against England and their old-time enemy,
Spain. But the common people in Holland were afraid of France. When
the French King, Louis XIV, an ever greedy monarch, suddenly played
false to John and descended with a mighty army to seize the Netherlands
for himself, the Dutch fell into a panic. They grew furious with John,
forgetting his years of faithful service.

It was John de Witt's correspondence with one of the ministers of
King Louis which Cornelius had entrusted to Van Baerle on the night
when Isaac was spying. Honest, and wholly devoted to Holland's best
interests, had John de Witt been, and these letters, calmly read in times to
come, would prove it, but publicly read in those days in the heat of panic

This picture was taken from an old print which hangs in the cell of Cornelius de Witt
in the Gevangenpoort at The Hague.

and prejudice, might easily be twisted and misunderstood as the intercourse of a traitor.

Now Van Baerle, as all his countrymen knew, was notably out of politics, a quiet student and tulip fancier, with no smallest thirst for glory. With him Cornelius de Witt had judged the papers would be safe. No matter what befell his brother John and himself, the letters would be preserved until the Dutch people were calm enough to read them with real justice.

Day by day, the de Witts grew ever more hotly hated. As the French advanced, the people demanded that William III, now grown a young man, be made Captain General of the armies. With irresistible force, the French took Gelderland, Utrecht and Overyssel and came to the very gates of Amsterdam. Then the people, seeing in William their only hope of deliverance, made him Stadtholder with unlimited powers, while John de Witt was forced to resign his office as Grand Pensionary.

At such a time as this, with feeling running so high, a wretched barber, named Tyckelaer, falsely announced that Cornelius de Witt had tried to hire him to murder William of Orange. Cornelius was dragged from his home in Dort and thrown into prison in the Gevangenpoort at the Hague. So enraged were the people, that they clamored to have him hung, but the court disappointed their savagery. It passed no more severe a sentence than life-long banishment from the land. On the day when Cornelius was to be released, John went to the prison to see him.

Before the gray walls of the grim old Gevangenpoort with its hideous grated windows, the waters of the Vyverberg lay calm and smiling, its green island glistening in the sun, its quiet blue like a mirror, reflecting the forms of the swans that floated majestically on its bosom. Across the pond the pointed gables af the ancient Gothic houses nestled peacefully beneath the shade of the noble trees. But, quiet as was all nature, the place was filled with an ominous murmur. A threatening mob stood about, whispering, sullen, waiting for the prisoner with murder in their hearts.

John sought Cornelius in his wretched, little cell, and knowing all too well the danger that confronted them, he asked his brother how he had disposed of his correspondence with France. If Van Baerle had it, let Cornelius write at once and order him to destroy it, lest men find it in his possession, and therefore, threaten his life. So Cornelius tore a flyleaf from his Bible and wrote a brief note to Van Baerle, bidding him burn, unread, the letters entrusted to him, that he might remain, as before, ignorant of what was in them.

Then John and Cornelius set forth. Alack, how sad is their story.

The crazy mob fell upon them and made an end of their lives,—two gallant, devoted gentlemen, struck down by panic, and prejudice, and cruel misunderstanding.

News of the tragedy reached the ears of Isaac Boxtel before it was known to Van Baerle. Here at last was his chance to ruin his hated rival. He hurried off at once to lay a formal complaint. Van Baerle, he said, had in his possession a packet which would prove him to have been acquainted wth the plot of the false de Witts.

And what was Van Baerle doing during all this miserable time? Van Baerle had just dug up the bulb which he knew would produce in the very next Spring, the great black tulip. He had divided the bulb into three and could think of nothing else. Even when the message arrived from his godfather, he deemed the matter of no importance and continued to fondle his bulbs, holding unread in his hands the fly-leaf from Cornelius's Bible. It was thus he was found by the officers sent on Isaac's complaint to arrest him. Bursting into the room, they dragged him away. He had only time to do up his precious bulbs in that letter from Cornelius. In the excitement of the moment, he thought of the letter only as a scrap of wrapping paper.

Soon Van Baerle found himself in that very cell in the Gevangenpoort, where Cornelius had been confined, and left to the mercy of a savage old jailor named Gryphus. How sad would have been his life had it not been for the care of Rosa, a lovely Frisian maiden, the daughter of old Gryphus. Rosa was kindness itself, Rosa was all loveliness, like the flower whose name she bore.

Van Baerle asserted that he knew nothing of the contents of the package which had been found in his drying room, but what proof could he give of his statement? Little did he know that the proof lay wrapped around his bulbs in his godfather's unread letter. And so he was condemnd to be hanged and he gave his precious bulbs to Rosa, telling her how to plant them and win the prize in the Spring. But on the very scaffold, William of Orange had compassion and changed the sentence to life imprisonment in the fortress of Loewestein.

And now Van Baerle, taken away to that lonely island prison, thought he had lost the two things which he loved more than aught else in the world,—a flower and a maiden, Rosa and his tulip. From the grated window of his cell, in the tall tower of Loewestein, he gazed longingly at the windmills of his native town of Dort which could be seen in the distance behind a forest of chimneys. His companions were only the pigeons that glistened in the sunshine on the gabled red roof below him, and now and then flew up high enough to settle on his window sill.

Thus many sad months passed by and then, imagine his joy. One day, Rosa appeared at his door. Old Gryphus, her father, had been transferred to the care of Loewestein. So Van Baerle had his Rosa again. Van Baerle had his tulips. Which did he love more dearly? He scarcely knew himself. All in good time, Van Baerle planted one of his bulbs in a cracked jar in his window where he could watch it grow. The second he bade Rosa plant in the garden. The third, still wrapped in the note from Cornelius de Witt, lay hidden in a drawer under Rosa's finest laces.

But as the Spring-time drew near, and the wind across the river Waal came in with a gentle warmth, bringing a smell of the earth to Van Baerle's grated window, there appeared at Loewestein, a suspicious and ugly stranger. Jacob he called himself but in reality he was Isaac. Having failed to find the bulbs in his neighbor's house at Dort, when Van Baerle was dragged away, the ugly old creature had followed him even here, intending still to procure them. He made friends with Gryphus over plentiful bottles of gin and pretended to have come a-courting the pretty Rosa. But when Gryphus fell asleep in his chair after supper, he spied on Van Baerle and Rosa. Stealthily he followed the girl when she went to prepare her garden. Once she pretended to plant the bulb to see what Jacob would do. Lo, he came and dug where he thought the bulb had been laid. Then she and Van Baerle knew,—they had a dangerous foe. Rosa, therefore, planted the bulb in her own little room, and guarded it with care, but in a moment of rage, old Gryphus destroyed Van Baerle's

plant just as it began to gladden his heart with a showing of green in the cracked jar on his window sill.

What would the poor prisoner have done had not Rosa's tulip blossomed? One day she brought it to the grating of his door where they often talked together. And it was as black as jet without a single blemish. In great excitement, Van Baerle bade her go at once and take the flower to Haarlem, his beautiful black tulip, his wondrous queen of flowers! But Isaac by means of a secret key, made his way into Rosa's room when she had gone out and stole the precious tulip. Exulting in a frenzy, he hurried off to Haarlem. Now the prize was his. The whole world should honor him and call him the discoverer of the wonderful black tulip. Throughout the ages that tulip would bear his name, the Tulipa Nigra Boxtellea!

Then all that Rosa could do, poor child, was to take the third bulb and follow the thief to Haarlem. Thus Van Baerle was left once more alone,—no Rosa and no tulip. To keep up his courage, he sang the song of the flowers that were so dear to his heart

"We're children of the hidden fire,
The fire that streams through the veins of the earth,
We're children of dawn and of dew,
We're children of the air,
We're children of the showers,
But, above all, we are children of the sky."

To the Burgomaster, van Systens, President of the Tulip Society, little Rosa told her story. But who would believe a simple Frisian maiden? Isaac had already arrived and claimed the tulip as his own. Still Rosa was not to be daunted. She sought out the Stadtholder, William III himself, and blushing with girlish modesty, she gave the third precious bulb into his princely hands. The young man unwrapped the package and what did he behold? He beheld not only the bulb, but the fly-leaf from the Bible of Cornelius de Witt, with that last letter of his which proved that his godson, Van Baerle, was absolutely ignorant of the contents of that fatal package for knowledge of which he had been condemned to life-long imprisonment. A two-fold victory for little Rosa! The pale young Stadtholder, deeply moved at seeing again the writing of Cornelius de Witt, who, he now believed, had been most unjustly murdered, dismissed Rosa with a handsome gift, bidding her appear at the tulip feast on the following Sunday in the dress of a Frisian bride. Thereafter, he sent off post haste for Van Baerle.

And now at last, May 15, 1673, came Tulip Sunday in Haarlem. Thither gathered all those tranquil souls who love a world in bloom. Having made manifest its taste for flowers in general, and tulips in particular, at a time when war and sedition filled men's minds, elsewhere, the lovely little town, full of trees and sunshine, meant to make the ceremony of conferring the prize for the great black tulip, a fete to live forever in the memory of mankind. How innocent and harmless was Haarlem's contest for glory! Haarlem had no conquerors except her triumphant florists. Only in honor of gardeners would she rend the air with cheers.

At the head of the procession marched Burgomaster van Systens in black velvet and violet silk, with linen of dazzling whiteness, carrying an enormous nosegay, and the heart in his bosom was innocent as the flowers he bore in his hand. After him came the committee of Horticulture, decked with gay colors like a flowery meadow and exhaling all the sweet perfumes of springtime. Later marched the learned societies of the town, the magistrates, the military, the nobles and the peasants. The procession was as placid as the passing of a flock of lambs on the earth, and as innocent of offense as a flight of birds through the air.

In the center of this peaceful, sweet-smelling train, rode the haughty black tulip itself, borne on a splendid litter, with a coverlet of white velvet, richly fringed with gold.

At length the procession stopped in a circle of fine old trees. Joyous music burst forth and the fairest damsels of Haarlem, like the guard of honor for a queen, came forward to escort the tulip to a raised seat on the platform where it was to stand beside the gilded chair of his Highness, Prince William himself. When it had been lifted into place, a clapping of hands and tremendous cheering awoke the echoes of Haarlem.

Now among the members of the Horticultural Society, all clad in scarlet, stood Isaac Boxtel, confident that he had won the prize, his mind still full of the wonderful thought that this tulip should bear forever his name, the Tulipa Nigra Boxtellea.

Then the tall, pale young Stadtholder rose and called aloud:

"Let the person approach to whom the black tulip belongs."

Isaac started boldly forward. But, before him, a soldier helped up a pretty Frisian girl in the costume of a Frisian bride, scarlet wool embroidered in silver and the finest of fine lace veils.

"This tulip is yours, is it not, my child?" said the Stadtholder kindly.

"Yes, your Highness," stammered Rosa. And through all the assembled crowd a murmur of pleasure burst forth at sight of her girlish beauty.

"Henceforth," said the Stadtholder, "this tulip shall be called,—" Isaac held his breath, but Prince William never faltered—"this tulip shall be called the Tulipa Nigra Rosa Baerlensis, because of the name of Van Baerle which will henceforth be the married name of this maiden."

And who is that young man stepping out of a traveling carriage, and pressing forward in wild excitement? It is Van Baerle himself.

"I am lost!" cried Isaac Boxtel, and he sank to the earth, senseless in his despair.

Then William took Rosa's hand and placed it in that of Van Baerle.

"Your innocence has been proved," he said to the young man before him. "And the prize of 100,000 florins belongs to you and your bride. You are the godson of Cornelius de Witt and the friend of his brother John. Remain worthy of the friendship with which they have honored you, for the de Witts, wrongly judged and wrongly punished in a moment of popular error, were two great citizens of whom Holland will always be justly proud."

After these words, which he spoke in a voice full of deep emotion, William III gave his hands to the lovers to kiss while they knelt before him. Then he said with a sigh:

"Alas, you are very happy, who, dreaming, it may be of the truest glory for Holland, attempt to conquer naught for her save only new colors for tulips."

This William III of Orange, through his right as grandson of Charles I of England, and likewise by right of his wife, Mary Stuart, daughter of James II of England, became in 1689 King of England, as William III.

THE TALE OF ECHO WELL
Hop, Mary Annikin,
Syrup cannikin,—
Make the dollies dance!
In this land once lived the Prince,
Now ragged men from France!
Hop, Mary Annikin,
Syrup cannikin,—
Make the dollies dance!
He'll rock baby and stir the gruel,
And make his doggie dance!

That was what poor young William the fifth, Stadtholder and Prince of Holland, sang to his baby son in 1794 when ragged men from France came pouring into Holland. In their own land these ragged men had done away with their king. They had shouted, "Down with kings!" And they had made themselves a republic with a president to rule them.

"Ah," the Dutch burghers cried as they heard these Frenchmen chatter about how fine it was to be free from the rule of kings, "Just listen! If we, too, could only have a republic!"

So they drove Prince William, his baby son and all his family off to England and they made themselves a republic. After that Father William, far away in England, hadn't a thing to do since he couldn't rule any more. He just kept rocking the cradle and bidding Mary Annikin hop to entertain the baby. He kept stirring the baby's gruel and making the doggie dance, while the ragged men from France, all tatters and

patches and pieces, kept marching around in Holland and shouting:

"Hurrah for the Dutch Republic! Hurrah! Hurrah! Hurrah!"

Well, so things went till the Emperor Napoleon wiped out the French Republic, dressed all the ragged fellows in shiny new uniforms and brought half Europe under his thumb. Then this strutting little Napoleon saw the pretty green fields of Holland and he said, "I'll take those, too." So he sent his brother, Louis Bonaparte, with the shiniest of his soldiers, to be the King of Holland, leaving poor Prince William still rocking his baby in England.

Very busy were those shiny French soldiers, doing this and that in Holland. They built a road here. They dug a well there.

One day in the year 1809, they dug a well at the foot of Earthman's Mountain in the Province of Gelderland. Far, far down they dug when all at once, to their great astonishment, they found the home of a little Dutch dwarf. Way down in the earth, they came on the earthman's tiny kitchen and there they learned a secret. The dwarf himself was not at home but the Frenchmen saw that there was a tiny lady, a very, very pretty little lady, locked up in his kitchen. There she sat, so pretty and so silent, for she made no sound at all.

Going up to the top of the well, the Frenchmen hailed some Dutch farmers who chanced to be passing down the road.

"What do you know about the dwarf who lives down here in the earth?" they asked the Dutchmen. "And what do you know about that pretty little lady he keeps locked up in the kitchen?"

The Dutchmen replied that the lady was the earthman's wife. For many years, they said, this little dwarf had lived in the Earthman's Mountain. During the day he never poked his nose out of the earth, but at night he would stir abroad on the heath, frightening good folks who passed by jumping suddenly out on the road before them or shouting unexpectedly from behind a bush or tree. Sometimes he was seen, by moonlight, stumbling over the heath on his crooked little legs, carrying a fagot, but no one had ever before found the entrance to his home.

Now his wife was the daughter of Air and Earth and was called Echo. She had once been a pretty girl, only far too talkative.

One time she could not stand it any longer at home, because Earth, her mother, never said a word, and if she spoke to her father, Air, he only whistled through the door crack, shouted through the chimney, or remained as deathly still as a motionless day in June.

So it happened that Echo fled from her home. Near the Earthman's Mountain she met the little dwarf, who immediately fell in love with her, and, against his usual custom, spoke to her very kindly.

Then Echo, who was not used to much at home, thought him a nice, jolly sweetheart, and she married him on the spot.

At first things went very well. They lived cozily enough in their spacious dwelling beneath the mountain, with tunnels and rooms and everything nice. But soon the former nature of the goblin came to the surface; he could not keep up for long, his comedy of loving husband.

Soon it was: "Echo, keep still, I don't like so much noise."

Then the talkative, but sweet little wife was silent for a while. In a few moments, however, she forgot what her husband had said and began to prattle anew. By-and-by it became a continuous quarrel between the two, until the nasty earthman locked her up in the kitchen, and forbade her to speak unless she was spoken to, and then only to answer in the fewest possible words.

Under this heavy punishment, Echo grew very submissive. It was many a year she had been there when the soldiers of King Louis found her; but she never spoke a word until they called out:

"Was the name of your father, 'Air'?"

Then she answered. "Air."

"Was your mother, 'Earth'?"

"Earth."

"What was the Earthman like when you married him of old?"

"Old."

"Do you love him or no?"

"No."

"Well, if a woman talks like that," the soldiers said to the Dutchmen, making ready to run away in a hurry, "we'd best leave the matter to you. As Frenchmen, we have no right to mix in Dutch family quarrels. Kindly report the matter to the nearest Dutch policeman. We bid you a very good day!"

The Little Man in the Dog-Cart

A Tale from the Province of Gelderland

IT happened when the Dutch had the Frenchman, Louis Bonaparte, ruling them that they got pretty tired of feeding and clothing all the French soldiers King Louis kept in their land. So when King Louis' brother, the great, little, strutting Napoleon, lost the Battle of Waterloo and was no more Emperor of France, the Dutch packed the French off home. Then they called for their very own prince, young William of Orange, who, as a baby, had been rocked in his cradle in England. Back to Holland came William as the first Dutch King of the Netherlands, while some of the peasants still wondered whether they wished to be ruled by a king, a stadtholder or a president.

And it chanced at this time that a little peasant lived alone in a little house on the heath near Apeldoorn in the province of Gelderland. Now this little peasant had a dog team as fine as any in the neighborhood, and he had a little cart which he always kept painted bright and clean. He was very proud of his dogs; he was very proud of his cart,— you may be sure of that. Aye, there were none such dogs as his in all the province of Gelderland! So said the little peasant.

Well, it happened one day that the little man was riding along the Arnheim road toward Apeldoorn and he was going like mad as usual, his dogs running for dear life and his cart appearing to fly along over the smooth brick pavement. All of a sudden he heard a roar and a rumble behind him. He looked around, and what should he see but the King's coach coming, with four magnificent horses and a rider on the back of each.

The first rider whistled.

"Make way! Make way!" he shouted. "Make way for the King!"

But the little man had no mind to make way. It was not so long that there had been Kings in the Netherlands. Had not Dutchmen for generations been governed by their Stadtholders? This was a new fangled business having Kings, a new-fangled business indeed. The little peasant said to himself that he had been first on the road and a King had no right to push a peasant into the ditch. A King was a man and a peasant was a man, so where was the difference? If his dogs could go faster than the King's horses, why shouldn't he stay on the road? But he had a keen sense of humor, that little peasant, he knew the right time to laugh! So he chuckled to himself as he urged his dogs to go faster, and he called back over his shoulder:

"I'll go on ahead to tell them in Apeldoorn that you're coming."

"What does that fellow say?" cried the King, poking his head out the window.

At first his riders dared not reply, but the King cried again with a louder voice:

"Tell me! What does that fellow say?"

Then the last rider hesitatingly made answer:

"The man will not get out of the road with his cart and he says he will go on ahead to tell them in Apeldoorn that Your Majesty is coming!"

At that, you may well believe, there was a pretty to-do! The King was in a rage.

"Pass the braggart!" he stammered. "Pass him on the instant!"

Thereupon the riders pressed the horses to greater speed. They clucked, they whipped, they urged, but the little man and his cart kept well ahead. He had only to speak to his dogs and they ran, it seemed, like the wind.

The King stood up in excitement, and poked his head further out the window, till he almost lost his balance, hanging over the sill.

"Go faster!" he shouted. "Pass him! Pass him! Pass him!"

But the little man was ahead and ahead he stayed, up hill and down dale, past forest and heath, rattlety bang on the road!

By-and-by, he went dashing into the village. Then he shouted very grandly as though he had been an outrider sent ahead on purpose to prepare the way for the King:

"Make room! Make room! The King is coming. The King is coming." And he started in merrily singing:

Two buckets of water hauling,
Two buckets a-pumping,
Wooden shoes a-clumping.
Girlie, on your wooden leg,
Ride out through the gate, I beg.
  O thud, thud, thud,
Rides the King through the mud,
And straight, straight, straight,
Rides the King through the gate.
  With a one, two, three!

Well, that was that! The little man had enjoyed the race and played his joke on the King, but the next day, what? Ah, the next day it was different! The next day there came a summons to Master Peasant. He must go to the palace. He must appear before the King!

And how did the little peasant like that? Not much! Nay, not at all!

"Now I shall catch it," he thought, and he wished that he had not been quite so smart and played a joke on the King.

He put on his new Sunday suit and his new wooden shoes, but his heart beat loudly as he set out for Het Loo where the grand, royal palace stood amid lawns and surrounding forests. The nearer he came to the place, the more slowly he dragged his feet.

At last he stood before the King. It was all very fine about him, very fine, indeed.

"Now I shall catch it," he thought again. "Perhaps the King will shut me up in a dungeon. Perhaps he will order me to be whipped!"

But the King's anger had cooled. He, too, was a man for a joke. He, too, knew the right time to laugh, and, besides, he liked sturdy independence whenever he looked upon it To the astonishment of the little man, the King received him kindly, complimented him on his dogs which could carry him faster than the King's fine horses with four fine riders, thanked him for the lesson he had taught him, and gave him twenty-five guilders besides as a reward.

Then the joke was on the little man. His mouth fell open so wide that a gnat flew in and perched on his tongue. He thought he must be dreaming. He pinched himself to wake up. But there in his hand he still beheld, too solid for ghostly visions, the twenty-five precious guilders. Well, the peasant said to himself that he guessed he liked to be ruled by a king if every king was as jolly as that. And it was no time at all before he was shouting along with all the rest of the Dutch:

"Long live King William! Long live the House of Orange!"

Contents

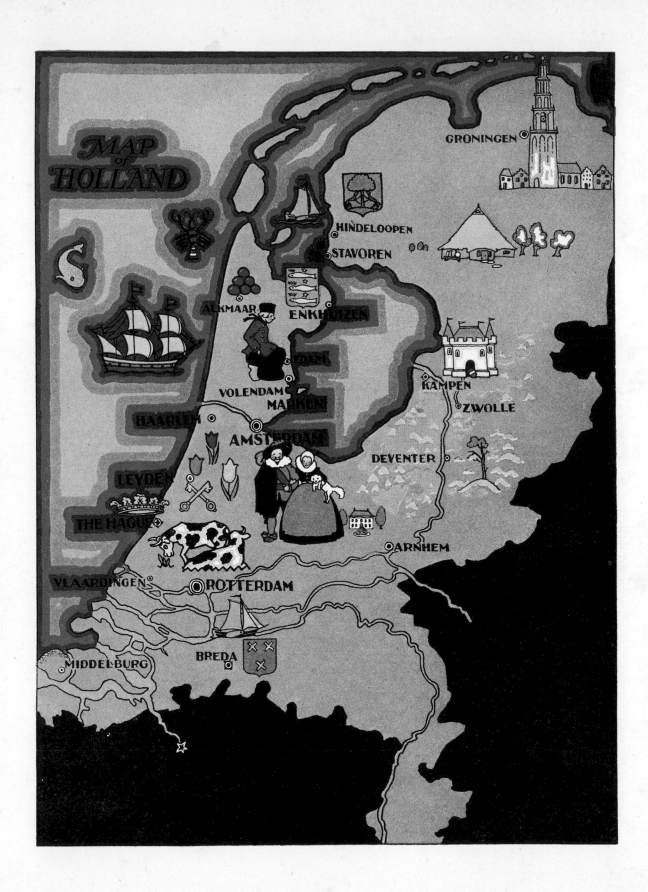